THE CONSUMMATE DENTAL HYGIENIST

Solutions for Challenging Workplace Issues

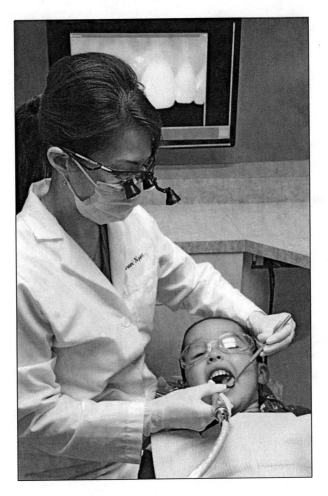

By Dianne Glasscoe Watterson, RDH, BS, MBA

The Consummate Dental Hygienist

Solutions for Challenging Workplace Issues

Cover Photo Credit:
Photo taken by Anne Nugent Guignon, RDH, MPH. Clinician is Dr. Lauren Nguyen. Other photos submitted by Anne N. Guignon include photos on pages 10, 22, 44, 48, 138, 152.
Cover photo modifications by Ted Anibal.

Disclaimer:

This book is designed to be informational about various situations that arise in daily practice. It is not meant to be regarded as "consulting advice." Obviously, the author cannot control variables or situations that arise between those in the dental office. The reader is urged to use the information presented herein by adapting it to his or her own individual practice. It is not the intention of this book to cover every nuance or practice situation that occurs in dental practices.

The author, publisher, or [Professional Dental Management, Inc.,] shall have neither liability nor responsibility to any person or entity with respect to any loss or untoward outcome caused directly or indirectly by information contained in this book.

Previous books by this author include *Manage Your Practice Well, Commonsense Practice Management Tools for the Dental Team*

Published by:

Professional Dental Management, Inc.
2825 Roderick Road
Frederick, MD 21704
www.professionaldentalmgmt.com

Book & Cover Design: Yvonne Pover, Creative Director
                       Skardon Pover, Inc.Visual & Marketing Communications

ISBN: 978-0-9844137-1-3

Dianne Glasscoe Watterson, MBA, CEO I www.professionaldentalmgmt.com I 301-874-5240

Professional Dental Management, Inc. I 2825 Roderick Road I Frederick, MD 21704

Dedication

My deepest thanks go to my husband who is my best friend, encourager, and wise confidant. He puts up with my hectic travel schedule and is understanding when I spend long hours in my office. His generous and kind spirit is an inspiration to me. I am blessed to have such a wonderful mate.

Love is patient. Love is kind. It does not envy; it does not boast; it is not proud. It is not self-seeking; it is not rude; it is not easily angered. It keeps no record of wrongs. Love does not delight in evil, but rejoices with the truth. Love always protects, always hopes, always trusts, always perseveres. Love never fails.

(I Cor. 13:4-8)

Table of Contents

Table of Contents

Acknowledgements

There are many people that I wish to thank for their contribution to my professional development over the years, starting with Dr. James McGhee of Thomasville, NC, who gave me my first job in a dental office when I was eighteen years old and totally new to dentistry.

To Teresa McRae, RDH, who had a tremendous influence on me as a coworker and the first dental hygienist I ever knew. I observed her outgoing, warm way with patients and how her patients absolutely loved her.

To Margaret Cain, RDH, Henrietta Andrews, RDH, Dr. Howard Blair, and Dr. Lundee Amos who were my hygiene instructors at Guilford Technical Community College.

To Dr. Hal A. Davis, my first boss as a young hygienist. Dr. D, you were and still are the BEST.

To Dr. Paul Keyes, who taught me back in the 1980's that I had tremendous power to help people with periodontal disease through non-surgical means. I came away from his lecture forever changed.

To Dr. E. T. Smith, Dr. Mike Lanning, and Dr. Diane Bundy who were such a joy to work with for many years in group practice in Thomasville, NC.

To Linda Miles, CSP, CMC, my dear friend and mentor in speaking/consulting. She gave me invaluable insight, direction, and most of all, friendship in transitioning into my own business.

To all my wonderful consulting clients scattered across the country.

To my wonderful husband, David, for enduring my hectic travel schedule. How blessed I am to have such a great spouse!

To my mom, Barbara Davis, for being my best friend and chief cheerleader all the days of my life.

To my fabulous editor, Mark Hartley. He gave me the "green light" to launch my *Staff Rx* column many years ago. I so appreciate his unwavering support of the dental hygiene profession.

To Ted Anibal, editor for this book and my previous publication entitled *Manage Your Practice Well*. Ted is a superb editor who can spot grammatical, punctuation, or sentence structure errors like no one I've ever known!

To Yvonne Pover, my graphic artist and friend. Yvonne is also a dental hygienist.

To the following dental hygienists that are dear friends: Anne Guignon, Jae Osborne, Cathy Seckman, Trisha O'Hehir, Laurie Pilson, Lynn Blatzheim, Kristie Bouldin, Lisa Surritte, and all my lister sisters/brothers on Amy's List and Hygienetown.

Preface

Dental hygienists as a group are some of the most caring, dedicated, meticulous people on earth. Hygienists have a desire to help people live healthy lives by taking care of the gateway to the entire human system—the oral cavity. Through their education and experience, dental hygienists have become the experts on prevention and excellent oral care. They have learned how to customize treatment and homecare instructions for individual patients, depending upon their needs. Hygienists are known for going the extra mile with patients in their quest for good oral health.

Dental hygiene is a great profession! What other profession allows so much one-on-one interaction with people? What other profession allows a working mom (or dad) the opportunity to work part time and still earn above-average wages? What other profession reaps the professional gratification of helping people transition from disease to health over a series of appointments? Indeed, dental hygiene has many unique rewards.

The education is rigorous, the work is hard, and sometimes the days are stressful. Communication challenges with bosses, coworkers, and patients force many hygienists to look beyond themselves to find equitable solutions. This is where I fit into the picture. Writing the "Staff Rx" column and various features for *RDH* magazine every month since April, 1998, has given me the "pulpit" to help hygienists with working dilemmas. This is my love, my passion—to help dental hygienists. I've never pretended to have all the answers. Some of life's most difficult dilemmas do not have easy solutions. But when I mentor a dental hygienist through a difficult situation or bring clarity to an issue, I know I have also helped a patient somewhere as well. I reap great personal satisfaction from that knowledge.

Dental hygienists persevere through it all for one primary reason—the sincere love and gratification that comes from helping people. This book is dedicated to dental hygienists far and wide. May God bless you in all your efforts to bring good oral health to your patients!

Dear Reader, this book is a compilation of feature articles and "Staff Rx" columns I have written since 2007. They have been chosen in the hope that you may find them enlightening and encouraging.

I begin with my tribute to Esther Wilkins, BS, RDH, DMD, because she is an icon of enlightenment and encouragement to all who have had the privilege of learning from her.

Dianne Glasscoe Watterson

The author (standing) poses with Dr. Esther Wilkins, Tina Potemken, and Lynn Blatzheim.

Tribute to Dr. Wilkins

The Grand Matriarch is a treasure!

My schedule changed at the last minute, making it possible for me to attend a lecture on clinical dental hygiene presented by none other than two renowned and beloved icons to dental hygienists everywhere—Esther Wilkins, BS, RDH, DMD, and Anna Pattison, RDH, MS. Dr. Wilkins has just completed the 10th edition of the dental hygiene textbook used throughout the United States. Pattison is an international lecturer and the co-author of Periodontal Instrumentation, a text used in dental hygiene schools nationwide, and is an associate professor at USC School of Dentistry.

It is difficult for me to put into words the deep admiration and respect I have for Dr. Wilkins. Her textbook (I have the dark blue one) guided me through hygiene school and became my primary roadmap in learning how to become a dental hygienist. Down through the years, we have crossed paths numerous times at dental meetings. I was first personally introduced to Esther many years ago when I spoke for the Massachusetts Dental Hygienists' Association. I was so honored to be seated next to her at dinner. After we were introduced, she told me that she always reads my columns in RDH magazine and that I was doing a great service to dental hygienists by addressing their real-life work issues. I'm sure I blushed! To be complimented by the author of my primary source of education in dental hygiene was the supreme compliment to me!

Sometime later, we were together for a weekend when Dentsply honored Esther and me along with four more dental professionals as "Distinguished Dental Professionals." How great it was for me to get to know her on a more personal level. It was there that I learned we shared a common tragedy—we had both been widowed.

Over the years, I have sought Esther's wise counsel on matters related to issues in my own professional life. She has always made time for me and gave an understanding ear. When I finished my MBA and wrote my Capstone Thesis on "Magnification in the Dental Industry," she asked to proofread my final paper and made some editing suggestions that brought clarity to my writing.

On Saturday, October 10, 2009 as I sat in her audience of approximately 300 people, I was deeply touched. Here stood a diminutive woman with snowy white hair who commands more respect than anyone in the profession. She may be small in stature, but she is a giant of a woman! She lectured in the old-school style with an overhead projector and illustrated her points with colored markers. She also used some PowerPoint slides to highlight particular points. Her ability to connect with the audience comes from her passion for teaching and her vast knowledge of the subject matter. Nobody does it like the master!

I saw a woman who loves dental hygienists so much that she cannot/ will not be content to fade into history. She could have retired many years ago to a life of leisure, but has chosen to keep doing the thing she loves most, which is teaching. Who do you know that is still working in her nineties? Her hand is steady, her mind is sharp, and her wit is quick.

Esther probably grows weary of hearing people say that she's a "treasure," but it is no less true! A treasure is something precious, valuable, and highly prized. Even those words seem inadequate to describe her worth to the dental hygiene profession. Dr. Esther Wilkins deserves all the accolades and praise that dental hygienists heap on her.

There is reference to another "Esther" in the Old Testament. She was described as a beautiful and daring queen who actually risked her life for the love of her people. Our present-day Esther is also a queen in her own right. She's beautiful through and through, bold and daring in the face of advancing age, and loves "her people"—dental hygienists everywhere. She deserves the title "Grand Matriarch of Dental Hygiene."

To this end, all of us who have benefitted from her wisdom humbly thank her for all she has done and continues to do for the profession of dental hygiene.

Dr. Wilkins with the author.

Chapter 1

Interpersonal Relationships: Patients

The profession of dental hygiene is uniquely "high-touch." It is highly personal physically, mentally, and emotionally. No dental professional spends more time with patients than the hygienist, and yet scant attention is paid to the importance of learning effective communication and understanding interpersonal relationships. As a result, interpersonal skills are largely self-taught with varying degrees of success.

Successful interpersonal relationships require constant effort because, frankly, people have their own problems, needs, and priorities. The needs of others usually take a back seat, and that is when conflicts can arise. This is not to say that one should ignore personal or professional needs, indeed, the individual is solely responsible for keeping his or her own "cup" filled. It does not depend on anyone else's approval, problems, or desires. Each one of us must control our own emotions, fulfillment of needs, and responses to conflict. Happiness is always an "inside job" whether we're dealing with ourselves, our patients, the boss, or coworkers. It all starts with you—the way you see yourself and the way you talk to yourself.

"Self-Image: How Patients Perceive You"

Every human being develops a mental image of him or herself over time that is the result of interactions with many people, including parents, siblings, teachers, and peers. Self-image has been described by educators with the famed Cleveland Clinic as "an internal dictionary that describes the characteristics of the self, including intelligent, beautiful, ugly, talented, selfish, and kind. These characteristics form a collective representation of our assets and liabilities as we see them." How you feel about yourself can and will affect the quality of relationships you form with patients, coworkers, family, and friends.

What Is Self-Image?

Self-image is our self-portrait. It is not necessarily what we see in the mirror, as that image may be real or distorted. The people with whom we shared close relationships while growing up sent us messages that were either positive or negative. If the messages were generally good, we are more likely to see ourselves as being confident, cheerful, and motivated. However, if there was a history of regular negative feedback, such as being oft criticized, teased or berated by others, we are more likely to struggle with poor self-esteem issues. From the Mayo Clinic: "When you have healthy self-esteem, you feel good about yourself and see yourself as deserving others' respect. When you have low self-esteem, on the other hand, you put little value on your opinions and ideas, and you constantly worry that you aren't good enough."

Our culture is intensely preoccupied with body image. Unfortunately, many people develop poor self-images because they are not able to achieve what they consider to be the "perfect" body. Mental illnesses, such as anorexia nervosa, cause the individual to see a distorted image when viewing his/her own body in the mirror. Some live lives of extreme rigor and discipline to maintain what they consider to be a superior body image. In addition to the physical self-image, every person has an emotional self-image.

When a person is unhappy with his/her body image, there is continual emotional discontent. Some have learned to be accepting of their physical appearance and have learned to tune out the negative cultural vibes. The outward body is the shell, but who we are resides inside. Choices we make have an impact on how we feel about ourselves. We can choose to be honest, moral, and caring, or we can choose to be dishonest, immoral, and uncaring. Those choices affect our emotional self-image.

The Pitfalls of an Overly High or Poor Self-Image

While it is best to be balanced, some people develop a self-image that is overly high. Such people develop an inflated sense of self-worth and often feel superior to others. These feelings can lead to arrogance or self-indulgence and make the individual feel he/she deserves special privileges. Dental professionals with an overly high self-image tend to evoke feelings of resentment and turn people off when attempting to engage in personal interaction. A dental professional with an inflated self-image may unknowingly cause those with whom they interact to feel inferior. They may carry on conversations that include over-the-top self-promotion, braggadocio, even backhanded compliments. For example, a dentist once commented on the company where a patient in his chair was employed by saying, "I see you work at 'XYZ Company.' I'm surprised a smart lady like you would work at a place like that." Needless to say, the patient was offended by this dentist's derogatory comment. (The patient was my mother.) It is typical for people who are filled with pride to disconnect from people whom they feel do not measure up to their level of superiority, i.e., "the little people."

At the other end of the spectrum are those with a poor self-image. When a person has a poor self-image, she sometimes develops a "poor me" complex. Such individuals often focus on their perceived weaknesses and give little credit to their own skills and assets. They feel they can never quite measure up. A dental professional with a poor self-image may have feelings of inadequacy and/or inferiority. These feelings, if pervasive enough, can be perceived by others to be aloofness or an uncaring attitude. Interestingly, a poor self-image can also elicit feelings of impatience, sharpness, defensiveness, unhappiness, even hostility. People with a poor self-image do not 'like' themselves, and deep down they cannot conceive why anyone else would like them. It is not unusual for people with a poor self-image to lash out at others.

Self-Image and Patient Communication

A healthy self-image is found in a position between the two extremes, not having an overly high self-image or a poor self-image. A person with a healthy self-image recognizes that he or she has good characteristics and also flaws. When a person understands his/her own worth, it becomes easy to respect others.

A dental professional's self-image can affect his/her ability to communicate effectively with patients and coworkers. A healthy self-image projects confidence, mental stability, assertiveness, and resilience. Dental professionals with a positive self-image are generally happy. Patients perceive when their caregivers are happy and well adjusted. Patients respond positively to caregivers who focus on their needs.

How Your Patients Perceive You

It is reasonable to assume that patients develop a perception of you based on many factors, which include your physical appearance, disposition, level of friendliness, level of caring, appearance of your operatory, and delivery of care. Is one factor more important than the others? Several patient interviews revealed some interesting perceptions. These questions were posed:

1. When you think of your dental hygienist, what first comes to mind?

2. How would you describe her appearance?

3. Is her appearance important?

4. How does she make you feel when you go in for preventive care?

5. Do you dread going to see your dental hygienist?

6. How would you characterize your most recent visit?

7. Anything else you'd like to add about your dental hygienist? Would you/do you recommend her to others?

Jillian (young professional)

"My hygienist is professional, not too stuffy, and she makes me feel relaxed and welcome. My dental hygienist always asks me if I'm flossing. I feel like I'm always being grilled about my homecare. I guess that's part of her job. I had bad dental experiences growing up and very bad teeth. So I have lots of anxiety about going to the dentist. I like the water tools she uses, and her chit-chat relaxes me. I drive 45 minutes to this office, and I have referred lots of friends and family. One of the things that impressed me most was that they sent a beautiful packet with information about the practice. Nobody made me feel ashamed of my ugly teeth. In fact, I feel OK about spending large sums of money to get good teeth. I plan to never leave this practice."

Sarah (hotel concierge)

"My dental hygienist is the 'motherly' type in a good way. She's a suburban mom, very professional and well-kept. I think she has to look good because she's a professional. Sometimes I feel guilty when she says, 'Wow, your gums

look great—I can see you've been flossing' when in fact I have NOT been flossing. I like her a lot."

Jenny (registered nurse)

"When I think of my dental hygienist, the first words that come to mind are capable, clean, and professional. Her clean appearance is important to me in particular since she will be working in my mouth. I never dread going to see her, as I know I'm doing a good thing for my own health. My visits are not rushed or prolonged but just right. I have recommended her to others. But one thing that makes me feel very uncomfortable is when she complains of not feeling well. If she's not well, she should not be working at all!"

Kay (CPA)

"When I think of my dental hygienist, my first thought is "Oh, no, not that time already!" Her appearance is very clean and professional. That's important to me, because if she had metal [piercings] all over her, I would be out of there! She makes me feel welcomed and she is friendly, except for one time when she insinuated that I hadn't kept my teeth brushed. The girl before her told me how nice I kept my teeth. I do dread going to see my hygienist because I have to have my teeth scraped and poked. I want my visits to be quick because I miss work. The office used to open at 7:00, which was more convenient. I don't want chatty, and I don't mind quiet. I don't recommend her to others, because I don't even know her name—isn't that a pity."

Steve (businessman)

"My dental hygienist is generally pleasant. Her appearance is important to me, because if she doesn't look together, what about her office and dental equipment? She makes me feel welcome and seems glad to take time with me. I never dread going to see her, and I have recommended her to others. My former hygienist was fired for always complaining."

In Conclusion

The way in which patients perceive their dental hygienist can affect the quality of communication and interaction. From the patient interviews, two factors stood out. (1) The appearance of the dental hygienist is important, and (2) what patients remember most is how their hygienist makes them feel. The way a dental professional feels about him/herself affects how patients feel about their provider.

Self-image is not static; it changes as a person matures and develops according to situations in life. Everyone goes through times when they feel insecure about their appearance, abilities, or accomplishments. It's when the negative feelings become long standing that self-esteem suffers. **A person's own thoughts have the most impact on self-esteem.** Fortunately, one's thought process is one aspect of self-image that can be controlled. People can learn to reframe negative thinking that tends to focus on their weaknesses or flaws.

The Cleveland Clinic outlines these specific steps to foster a positive self-image:

- Take a self-image inventory
- Define personal goals and objectives
- Set realistic and measurable goals
- Confront thinking distortions
- Identify childhood labels
- Stop comparing yourself to others
- Develop your strengths
- Learn to love yourself
- Give positive affirmations
- Remember that you are unique
- Learn to laugh and smile
- Remember how far you have come

A healthy self-image enables dental professionals to form secure and honest relationships and be less prone to feelings of hopelessness, worthlessness, and shame. Because self-esteem affects every facet of life, having a healthy, realistic self-view is important. A healthy self-image starts with learning to accept and love ourselves. It also means being accepted and loved by others.

References
http://www.mayoclinic.com/health/self-esteem/MH00128
http://my.clevelandclinic.org/healthy_living/mental_health/hic_fostering_a
_positive_self-image.aspx

"The Value of Attitude"

Over the years traveling across the country speaking and consulting, I have become acquainted with many dentists and hygienists who are very unhappy. The reasons are quite varied, but a few of the most prominent reasons are: perfectionism, personality clashes, financial problems, poor health, sour attitude, disharmony in the home, never being satisfied, and unmet expectations. I believe there are people who have been unhappy so long that they have forgotten how to be happy.

Some doctors and hygienists come to work carrying all kinds of emotional baggage. Some cannot wait for someone to ask if anything is wrong, because this gives the person the opportunity to 'vomit' up all their problems and spew them on anyone within earshot. Unhappy people like company! They readily recruit others to be unhappy with them.

Another tactic of unhappy people is to play the 'silent' game and keep everyone speculating about what could be wrong. They wear their unhappiness like a badge of honor, and their non-verbal communication shouts I'M NOT HAPPY! "Did you see how doc is acting today? I'll bet he had another fight with his wife…" "Something must be wrong with Mary. I could see it on her face when she walked in the door!"

Some doctors are so into perfectionism that staff members—no matter how hard they try—can never meet the doctor's level of expectation. These same doctors rarely, if ever, proffer a good word about staff job performance, but readily give out criticisms. Some just keep their frustrations bottled up, because they do not know how to tactfully discuss job performance with their staff members. As the bottled-up frustration builds, an explosion is inevitable resulting in a staff member leaving in anger and tears, which lead to—guess what—more unhappiness for the doctor.

Some hygienists are disenfranchised with everything about their work. They dislike their jobs, their coworkers, their doctor/employer, and to be honest, if there was anything else they could do that paid as well as dental hygiene, they would get out in a heartbeat. They go to work to get through the day and make another buck. Some people call that condition 'burnout,' but 'copout' might be a better word. People who are chronically unhappy are eventually unhappy in any life circumstance.

If the only satisfaction you receive from your work is your paycheck, you are, of all people, most miserable. The reality is that we need money to pay our bills and live, but money alone will not bring lasting happiness. Just ask any of the countless unhappy rich people in the world! Happiness is an attitude of the heart that is closely tied with being thankful.

Here's my advice for chronically unhappy doctors and hygienists—GET OVER YOURSELF! Get over being insecure, grumpy, hateful, explosive, touchy, unfriendly, perfectionistic, sour, impatient, dissatisfied, disloyal, uncaring, greedy, dishonest, unthankful, or whatever bad attitude you carry. To do this, you need to part with some of the stuff in your life. It is time to clean out your emotional closet and get rid of the junk that has accumulated there!

We all need to be thankful for our profession and the abilities we have to help people. We in dentistry have a unique opportunity every day with every patient who crosses our paths to be more than a caregiver but also a friend. We can develop connected, lasting relationships that people remember long after the dental care is over. What's wrong with being a bright spot in someone's day? What's wrong with being supportive and caring of each other?

We need to live our lives with an attitude of thankfulness every day. Doctors, you should be thankful every day for your staff members, because they are the most valuable asset you have. You may doubt that statement, because you consider your skill to be your most valuable asset. Maybe you should consider that you have limited/no ability to use that skill without the help of your staff members.

I recently visited a doctor I worked with as a young hygienist many years ago who is recovering from a stroke. His speech has been affected from the stroke, but with slow, deliberate words he said, "Dianne, I hope you tell all your doctor/clients that their staff is the most valuable asset they have. Of that, I am sure."

Hygienists, you need to be thankful every day for your jobs. For the most part, it is the doctor's efforts and money that have provided you with a place to work. You should respect and support the doctor as the owner of the practice and the one who signs your paycheck.

If the doctor has wounded you with harsh words and made it difficult for you to respect him/her, at least respect the position. No one is forcing you to work in any particular office. Make the doctor glad you are there, and provide the patients with the most excellent care possible.

Doctors and hygienists, if you are struggling with financial troubles, deal with the problem by getting professional help, making a plan, and sticking to it. Don't take your frustrations out on your coworkers or family. If your problems are marital, again, help is available for you, but do not bring your family problems to work. When you come in the door, leave your emotional baggage outside. We all make mistakes and mess up occasionally, but our problems are *our* problems.

Do you need an attitude adjustment? Do you need to step back and re-focus your sights on what is really important, what brings real happiness? Do you need to start treating your coworkers better and put aside petty differences?

Consider these wise words by Chuck Swindoll, Chancellor of the Dallas Theological Seminary:

"The longer I live, the more I realize the impact of attitude on life. Attitude, to me, is more important than education, than money, than circumstances, than failures, than successes, than what other people think or say or do. It is more important than appearance, giftedness, or skill. It will make or break a company...a church...a home. The remarkable thing is we have a choice every day regarding the attitude we embrace for that day. We cannot change our past...we cannot change the fact that people act in a certain way. We cannot change the inevitable. The only thing we can do is play on the one string we have, and that is our attitude...I am convinced that life is 10% what happens to me and 90% how I react to it. And so it is with you..."

Develop an attitude of a thankful and caring heart that is 'others' focused and not 'me' focused. When you do this, happiness takes root and grows.

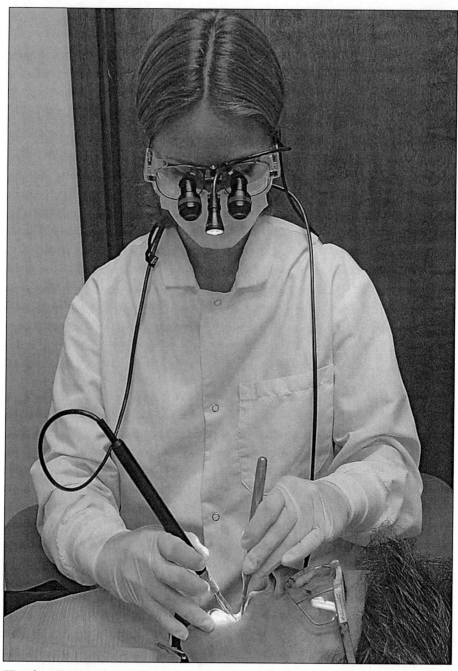

Heather Knitter, RDH, demonstrates proper operator and patient posture.

"Is this all there is???"

Dear Dianne,

I have worked in the same practice for 30 years. Our practice is part of a large group of practices. We just had our yearly review, and I am so disappointed! I was told that my salary is "capped out," which means I am making the maximum allowable wage. I have also been "capped out" for five years on vacation days.

I have a huge following of faithful patients, and when I get cancellations, I work hard to fill openings. What really frustrates me is that I work with two young hygienists who waste their downtime by browsing on the Internet or talking on the phone. We have cancellations every day, but I'm the only one who tries to fill openings. The doctor doesn't say anything.

At the review I tried to "plead" my case that I produced $13,000 more last year than the other girls. I bring a lot of experience and personality to our practice. They wholeheartedly agreed and actually apologized that I was only getting a 1.7% raise, while the other girls got 3.5%.

I am so sad. I know I got a little raise, but the incentive is just not there anymore. I feel like "slacking" like the other girls, but my work ethic won't let me. I do love my job and the girls at the office get along well. Do I just work the next 10 years at making no extra money? Please help me see through this dilemma.

Frustrated RDH

Dear Frustrated,

Actually, anyone who stays at a job long enough will (most likely) hit the salary peak for his/her job class. That does not mean there will not be any more raises. It just means the raises will be small cost-of-living increases. Dental practices are no different from other businesses that struggle with keeping overhead costs under control. Typically, the staff percentage of overhead is the largest overhead category.

I believe your office did you and the practice a disservice by telling you that you have 'capped out.' By telling you this, they de-valued your contribution to the practice, and worse, de-motivated you to work to your highest potential for the good of the practice. It is unfortunate that corporations are so focused on the numbers that they forget that employees are not numbers, that all staff members do not bring the same value to the business. Most likely, the doctor is an employee of the corporation and may feel unempowered or unmotivated to address work ethic issues. I believe high performers should be rewarded above average performers. I think the idea of random bonuses for stellar performance is a good way for management to reward long-term staff members who have reached the top of their job class pay. How much better it would have been if they had congratulated you on a wonderful year of being the highest producer and given you a bonus you were not expecting, along with your cost-of-living raise!

The dental hygiene profession has a kind of unspoken "glass ceiling" which means there is really no way to move up the ladder and nowhere else to go to advance in the profession UNLESS the hygienist is willing to go back to school and increase his/her education. The sadness and hopelessness you felt occurred as a result of bumping your head on the 'glass ceiling.'

Job satisfaction is not all about the money, but I don't have to tell you that. You didn't stay 30 years in this profession strictly for the money. And as far as what your coworkers make, that is irrelevant to the current dilemma. Your practice and patients are so blessed to have you, and I congratulate you for your amazing longevity. I believe you when you say you love your job.

I believe many of us come to a point in our lives when we wonder, "Is this all there is?" For me, it was when I was 39 years old. I had been a clinical hygienist for 18 years. I went back to school and earned a bachelor degree while working part time. Then I went back to school again and earned an MBA. I loved my patients and enjoyed the challenges of patient care, but I felt the need to expand my options.

If you want to see how your pay stacks up against other states, there are a couple of resources: http://www.dentistryiq.com/index/Hygiene_Department/salaries.html. or http://www.salary.com. Check it out.

My pay as a hygienist was infinitely better than when I was a chairside assistant or a business assistant making $350/month before taxes (1972). From that perspective, the average hygiene pay with benefits is not bad.

It would be a great thing for all of us to aspire to be like the Apostle Paul. He proclaimed in his teaching to the Philippians, "I have learned in whatsoever state I am, therewith to be content." What he meant is he had learned to be content with whatever life threw his way, good or bad, rich or poor, sick or well, abundance or need. He knew real happiness was not based on how much money he made.

The only other thing I would add is that we are living in very uncertain economic times. Many businesses, including dental practices, are seeing negative growth at the bottom line. When that's the case, practices cannot pay out more. They have to be able to keep costs under control and try to weather economic downturns. Bankruptcies have already occurred in many dental practices across the country. Think about it. Have you ever seen a time when dentists are losing their jobs due to business failure?

So what are your options? Well, here's the way I see it:

(1) Go back to school. Make a future plan. Decide where you'd like to be in five years.

(2) Keep your eyes and ears open for hygiene openings and change jobs. I know you'd hate to leave your patients, but my experience is that you form connected relationships with new patients, too.

(3) Remember Paul's words and think of how thankful you should be to have a job that you like. Do your best—just like you always have—without complaining and make your employer glad you are there. Keep your eye focused on why you are there to start with, i.e., to provide excellent care to those people who entrust their care to you. Don't let your coworkers distract you, but know that the young ones are watching you every day without your knowledge. Be a caring mentor to them.

I hope my words help you put this situation in perspective. I don't have any magic bullets, but as with most things in life, you do have some choices. Life should be more about being content, because as we all know, life is certainly not fair.

Best wishes,

Dianne

"Breaking the Bad News"

Dear Dianne,

Recently, a dentist in our town died. He had been practicing for 45 years and never employed a hygienist. He worked out of a small office with two chairs and only had one assistant who worked at the front desk and at chairside. This dentist was quite a charismatic person and well liked around town. He had a large and loyal patient base.

After his death, many of his patients started coming to the office where I presently work. Almost to the patient, every one of his former patients we have seen has periodontal disease. It appears that this doctor never scaled subgingivally at all! These are patients that received regular care from him for a long period of time.

The dilemma for us is that when we tell his patients that they need to have periodontal treatment, they view us with suspicion. Several have made the comment, "Dr. XXX never told me anything like that, and I went to him for years!" It makes me feel bad that they might think we are lying to them, possibly for financial reasons.

Do you have any suggestions on how we can break the bad news to patients like this who have been receiving substandard care elsewhere without disparaging the previous clinician?

Caught in a Dilemma

Dear Caught,

I'm glad you wrote about this situation, because I'm certain many of your peers across the country have experienced a similar scenario.

Failure to diagnose periodontal disease is #5 in the top 10 reasons dentists are sued, according to Dr. Crystal Baxter, a prosthodontist and expert witness and consultant in over 300 lawsuits against dental professionals. She further states that in the majority of these cases, there were no current radiographs or periodontal chartings, and many of the cases she reviewed were practices that never employed a hygienist.

There is a problem with the periodontal identification process in some practices. When hygienists are time pressed and are forced to work with inadequate time, one of the first things to go right out the window is periodontal charting. This is especially true if there is no one designated to record periodontal chartings. The time needed to do a six-point probing and recording solo is anywhere from 10–12 minutes, whereas with an assistant recording probings as they are called out, it takes only 3-5 minutes. When charting is not being performed regularly, periodontal disease can go on unnoticed for months, even years.

Further, since I brought up the issue of probing, every adult patient in the practice should have a six-point probing with ALL numbers recorded (yes, even numbers below 4 mm) a minimum of once/year. The reason that all numbers should be recorded is that if the chart is ever called into question in a court of law, a periodontal charting with only a few numbers scattered here and there looks like an incomplete charting to a jury. In the eyes of a jury, the rule is this—if it is not recorded in the chart, it did not happen. I would use this same logic to build a case against using the PSR method of probing. It is incomplete at best and should only be used as a screening device.

In the situation you have described, the dentist was obviously not practicing preventive care according to the current standards of care. Since periodontal disease can go unnoticed by patients for years, his patients have been completely unaware of their problems. Although the original dentist has passed away, he could still be sued. His patients placed their trust in him to take care of their dental needs, and he did not do that. That is called 'supervised neglect.' The risk for him now is that some patient will sue him after learning the truth about the periodontal disease that exists now and has existed for a considerable amount of time.

However, it is unproductive and unethical to disparage another health-care provider, especially since the substandard care is in the past. What is done is done. Your challenge is to help these patients achieve and maintain good oral health by giving them the appropriate care they need now. You have to help them understand that they have an active disease that requires more than just a 'flick and polish' to become healthy again.

Let's set forth a strategy that you and your colleagues can use when circumstances like this arise. Let's call it the 'red flag' strategy. However, before we delve into the specifics, let's dream of the ideal scenario.

In a faraway land called "Dental Hygiene Utopia," new adult patients see the doctor first, have their complete examination—both periodontal and restorative—with any necessary radiographs, and the diagnosis is made and explained to the patient. The patient understands and accepts the treatment recommendations. When the patient comes to the hygiene department, the road map has already been developed, and the hygienist is ready to begin necessary therapy. What a beautiful dream, but as dreams go, they rarely come true!

Let's assume that new patients are first scheduled in the hygiene department in your practice. The new patient is seated in your chair. You complete all the necessary preliminary functions—introductions, medical history review, blood pressure screening, intraoral and extraoral assessments, and radiographs. Next, you pick up your periodontal probe and begin your charting. (Ideally, you have an assistant to record probings.) You can see some significant subgingival deposits on the radiographs, and you see bleeding upon probing. Now is the time to 'raise the red flag.'

You say, "Mrs. Jones, have you noticed this particular area bleeding when you brush?" A little more probing, then you say, "Have you noticed this area being inflamed?" Now is the perfect time to engage your intraoral camera to let the patient see exactly what you are seeing in his/her mouth. In the absence of an intraoral camera, pointing out calculus and/or bone loss on an X-ray is also recommended. All you are doing is calling attention to the obvious (at least obvious to you!) Then you lay down your probe and say, "Mrs. Jones, according to what I see in your mouth and on these X-rays, there appears to be some problems with your gums and even the bone around some of your teeth, and before I proceed any further, I need the doctor to come in and have a look." You have raised the red flag!

Then you leave the operatory to go and inform the doctor about your findings (out of the patient's hearing) and request a brief doctor examination. Most likely, you have interrupted the doctor with his/her patient, so an extensive exam should not be expected at this point. When the doctor enters the room, introduce the patient to the doctor. Then the doctor will sit down, look at the X-rays, and perform a cursory exam. Then the doctor should say, "Mrs. Jones, from what I see in your mouth and on these X-rays, **you have periodontal disease. It is a chronic infection** in your gums, and over time, it destroys what supports your teeth, namely the gums and bone. Your teeth are like fence posts in the ground. As long as the earth around those posts is strong and firm, the posts will stand nice and straight. But if the earth around the posts deteriorates or falls away, the posts get loose. That's what happens in the mouth, too. The disease in your mouth is destroying what supports your teeth. The good news is we know how to treat this disease and get it under control, usually in a non-surgical manner."

Painting word pictures with analogies will help patients understand the disease process. Another good analogy is the way termites can undermine the foundation of a building.

At this point, the patient may make any number of comments like, "No one has ever told me this before," or "Dr. XXX never told me this before." This comment is really saying, "I'm not sure I can trust you," which is a natural reaction for a first visit. One visit is seldom sufficient to build a bond of trust between a patient and a clinician. You should not take offense when a patient makes this observation. Rather, you should say, "Really? Well, we're very glad you are here today, because it is obvious there have been some changes since your last visit." The point is all you know is what you see today! For you, whatever happened in the past regarding care is not your concern. The overriding concern is getting this patient back to good health.

Patients are not stupid! If the patient has been receiving substandard care, let him figure that out on his own when he sees the difference in his former care compared with the care you deliver.

If the patient protests that all s/he wants is a 'cleaning,' another analogy works well, and that is the 'infected wound' analogy. "Mrs. Jones, if you had a gash on your arm that was infected, would putting a Band-Aid® on it help it heal? Infections have to be treated appropriately to get better, and a mere cleaning is inappropriate for your condition. It would be like putting a Band-Aid® on an infected wound. Actually, 'cleanings' are appropriate for people with healthy gums, and unfortunately, yours are not. But the good news is that we know how to get your gums healthy again, and that is with the right treatment."

Your challenge is help the patient build a bridge of understanding in her own mind between a mere cleaning and treating an active infection in her mouth. But what if the patient refuses your treatment recommendation for definitive periodontal treatment? Ah yes, that's fodder for another column! Stay tuned!

I hope the aforementioned tips will help you improve your protocol when dealing with patients who have previously received substandard care. Stick to what you see today, and major on what is needed to help this patient return to a measure of good oral health.

Best wishes,

Dianne

The Consummate Dental Hygienist

"Angry Patient"

Dear Dianne,

Recently I had a new patient in my chair. When I did my initial assessment and periodontal probing, I noted several areas of pocketing and generalized bleeding. He had had no care for several years, and he presented with moderate periodontal disease. I explained to the patient that he had periodontal disease and needed root planing and scaling to bring the disease under control. The patient seemed agitated and stated that all he wanted was to get his teeth cleaned. When I explained that a 'cleaning' was not the appropriate treatment for periodontal disease, he became angry. He jumped up from the chair, ripped his patient napkin off, and as he was storming by the front desk, he declared, "I'm going to sue this practice!"

The front desk assistants and I were shocked by his outburst! Now I'm left feeling like maybe I didn't do something right. I've never had anything like this happen before, and I certainly do not want to be the reason for a patient lawsuit. Could this patient really sue us? What should I have done differently?

Worried and wondering

Dear Worried,

Here in America, anybody can sue for almost anything. However, the success of any lawsuit brought against a dental professional is determined largely by the quality of the chart notes. I hope you thoroughly documented your findings and the patient's response. I would advise you to use quotation marks when recording remarks the patient actually said.

Certainly, clinicians have the right to refuse to render inappropriate treatment.

However, let's go back to the actual appointment. Your office protocol is typical of many offices that see new patients in the hygiene department first. I understand the reason many doctors use this protocol is because hygienists are excellent at gathering data and performing assessments. It is preferable for adult new patients see the doctor first for a thorough examination and periodontal charting.

My feeling is that the patient's response might have been different had the pronouncement of periodontal disease come from the doctor instead of you. In the future, I would advise that you change your protocol for new patients and allow the doctor to deliver the diagnosis of periodontal disease. The best way to do that is to gather all the necessary data, arrive at an initial periodontal classification, then have the doctor come in and confirm the assessments and co-diagnosis.

Obviously, this patient was upset that he didn't get his teeth 'cleaned' at the initial visit. With a new patient, there is no way to know for sure what the patient needs in terms of preventive care before the assessment is performed. Some new patients will only need a prophylaxis, but others will need more definitive care. Your business assistants should inform new patients who want to get their teeth cleaned on the first visit that there are several different levels of preventive care, and the level needed will be determined after the examination.

"Mrs. Jones, since we've never seen you before, I don't know what level of preventive care you need. That will be determined after your examination. We tailor our treatment based on patient need." If a new patient needs periodontal therapy, I think it is wise for the hygienist to scale a limited area and use the code #4342 (root planing/scaling 1-3 teeth) on the first visit. By doing this, at least the patient feels s/he has had some scaling done.

Consider what you would have done if, instead of causing a scene, the patient told you in a regretful way that he could not afford perio-dontal care right now. What would you have done under that circumstance? In that case, I would have probably done a full-mouth debridement with a power scaler and documented well that the patient declined definitive care for his periodontal condition. After all, *some* **care is better than no care.**

This particular patient's expectation was that he was to get his teeth 'cleaned,' but his expectation was not met. However, his expectation was not reasonable, based on his periodontal condition. It is certainly not your fault that he had neglected his teeth over time to the point of developing periodontal disease.

Using appropriate analogies is a great way to help patients understand the disease process at work in their mouths. For example, you could have said: "If you had pneumonia and your physician wanted to treat you for a common cold, would you think something was wrong?" Or, "If you had an infected wound on your arm, would merely putting a band aid on it make it get well? Doing a mere 'cleaning' on someone with periodontal disease would be like putting a band aid on an infected wound."

Our world is not ideal, and sometimes in dentistry we have to provide less-than-ideal options for our patients. Consider the patient who has fractured a molar and needs a crown on the tooth. What would the doctor do if the patient states he simply cannot afford to have a crown done right now? Would the doctor send the patient away with no care? Probably not. The doctor would probably provide a 'less-than-ideal' option, such as a temporary crown or a large restoration.

So, here are my suggestions:

1. Improve the communication between the business assistant and the new patient at the time the initial appointment is scheduled.

2. When periodontal disease is present, have the doctor come in and deliver the definitive diagnosis.

3. If the patient's expectations are unreasonable, you may be able through good verbal skills to adjust the expectations. Use analogies to get the point across.

4. Patients are not to dictate care, but we have to operate within the boundaries set by the patient. Patients do have a right to refuse care, just as we have a right not to render inappropriate care.

5. Remember that you can't please everyone, but you can try.

Best wishes,

Dianne

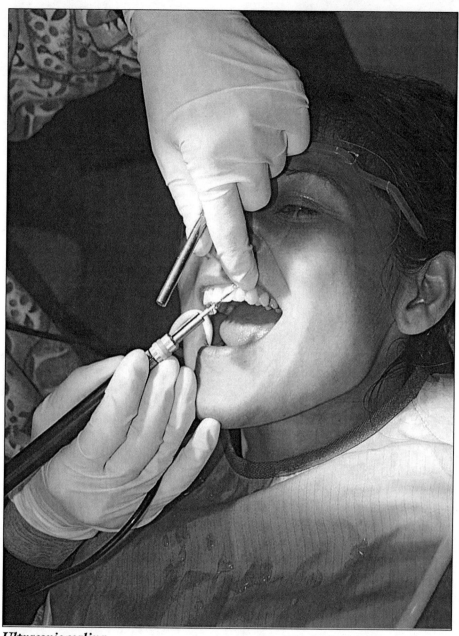

Ultrasonic scaling.

Chapter 2

Interpersonal Relationships: Coworkers

"Coworker Criticism"

Dear Dianne,

I graduated from hygiene school six years ago. Currently, I work in a two-doctor, three-hygienist practice. The problem I am writing about has to do with one of the other hygienists in the practice. She has been practicing over 20 years, and it is logical to think that with all that experience she would be a superb clinician. I wish it was true! The fact is, the quality of her work is poor. She rarely uses her power scaler, and her instruments are always dull. Her sharpening method seems strange to me—she keeps the stone stationary on the table and moves the instrument across it.

Recently, I was asked to complete a root planing patient that she had begun. The chart notes indicated she had completed both quadrants on the right side. I found so much subgingival calculus that I wound up rescaling both right side quadrants at no charge to the patient.

I do not know what to do about this situation. Should I mention something to the senior doctor? Should I say something to my coworker directly? I feel very uncomfortable saying anything to her because of our age difference. Should I just live and let live? I want to do the right thing.

Florida Hygienist

Dear Florida,

The fact that one graduates from a dental school or hygiene school does not automatically guarantee a lifetime of clinical competency. Graduation indicates the clinician has reached a certain level of competency at that point in time, which ensures a foundation of knowledge on which to build. It is like building a house. We have to start with a foundation and build the structure from the ground up. Some people keep on building and adding to their house through the years, while some never progress very far beyond the bare basics.

Providing competent clinical care means learning new things and moving forward as the knowledge base grows and changes. If I continued to practice like I did in 1978 (the year I graduated from hygiene school), I would rarely use ultrasonics except on gross calculus cases; I would not wear gloves; I would still believe mechanical friction is required to remove plaque; I would never use anesthesia; I would still be doing the old gross scaling/fine scaling routine; I would believe that the patient's level of oral hygiene would determine success or failure; I would be ignorant of the role of host immune response and the many systemic factors associated with periodontitis; and I would believe that bleeding is always a sign of disease.

When it comes to complete calculus removal, the fact is this: Rarely, if ever, do we remove every last spicule. (Brayer, WK, et al. "Scaling and root planing effectiveness: the effect of root surface access and operator experience." *J Periodontol.* 1989 Jan; 60(1):67-72.) Even periodontists will admit that laying a gingival flap and being able to see the root surface directly does not ensure complete calculus removal. If we think we have removed ALL the calculus, we delude ourselves. Remember this: It is always easier to see the dirt in someone else's house than in my own house, meaning it is easy for us to be critical of other people's work.

However, there is a difference in leaving a few little spicules and leaving large chunks of easily detectable calculus. What you described sounds more like the latter scenario. We can only speculate about the reasons for such incomplete calculus removal, such as dull instruments, incorrect instrumentation, etc. The most important consideration in this discussion is patient care. It is our licensure mandate that we treat our patients with a level of competence needed to help the patient attain a high level of oral health. If we cannot do that, we need to refer the patient to someone who can.

One way to look at this situation is by approaching the dilemma as if you were the one leaving the calculus. If I were leaving so much calculus behind that my coworker had to rescale the areas I had recently scaled, I would want to know about it. How can I fix something that I do not know is broken? How can I improve if I do not know there is a problem?

I do not feel involving the doctor would be the answer, at least initially. What can he do? He did not see the problem first hand. If he discussed the problem with your coworker, he would have to say something like, "It has come to my attention that you are leaving excessive calculus deposits…" The coworker would know that either you or the other hygienist had brought the matter to him first without consulting her.

Here is my suggestion on what to say:

"Mary, something happened the other day that I think you should know about. I have given this a great deal of consideration and have wrestled with whether to say anything or not. I believe you would want to know and have a right to know. Do you remember a patient named xxxxx? I was asked to complete his RPS because he had to change his appointment. The chart indicated you had completed the right side scalings. However, I had to rescale the right side because of missed calculus. I know I don't always get it all off either, but I just thought you'd like to know. I hope you will take this in the spirit it is offered, and that is as your friend."

This is certain to be a shock to your coworker, but she needs to know. This situation will demand as much tact and grace as you can muster. Always consider how you would feel if you were the other person. The fact that she is older should not prevent you from helping her.

Telling her is the hard part. Afterward, you may get an opportunity to help her with her sharpening technique. Also, you may get to help her expand the use of power scalers. My favorite inserts are the thin magnetostrictive inserts that can be used on high power, such as the Burnett Power Tip® by Parkell, or the new Dentsply SlimLine®. It sounds like she has allowed her clinical skills to stagnate over time. We all need to continually challenge ourselves to become better. When we rest, we rust.

Personally, I have never met a dentist or dental hygienist who feels he/she does substandard work. I believe most dental professionals take pride in their work and feel they have provided valuable services to their patients. However, it is no great revelation that all clinicians do not attain or maintain the same level of competency. When someone's clinical competency becomes questionable, patient care suffers. Doing the 'right thing' in this situation means calling attention to a problem that needs to be remedied in an effort to ensure the delivery of high-quality patient care.

Best wishes,

Dianne

Four entrepreneurial hygienists: Marie Wickman-Dykes, inventor of Mirror Gear®; Becky Logue inventor of the Dental RAT®; Vonda Manley, inventor of Edge-Ease®; and Ann Arrington, inventor of the Blue Boa®

Mirror Gear®

Blue Boa®

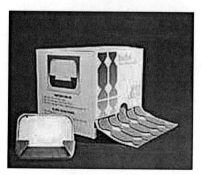

Edge-Ease®

Dental RAT®

"Workplace Bullying"

Dear Dianne,

I graduated from hygiene school two years ago and accepted a position in a local dental practice. I really love dental hygiene, but my work is becoming increasingly difficult because of bullying from a coworker. She is a dental assistant who has worked in the practice for about 10 years. For some reason, her bullying has increased lately, and I've left the office in tears on several occasions. I try to avoid her, but in our small office, that's impossible.

The first time it happened, I was speechless. She approached me in the staff lounge at lunch and made a cutting remark about my hair. Looking back, I should have cut her right back, but I was so shocked that I didn't know what to say. Now she says things like, "You really think you are something, don't you? I think you're a piece of @#$%!" When I asked what I had done to make her feel that way, she said she had a right to feel any way she wishes. She makes no bones about the fact that she does not like me. She's about twice my size, and I'm actually afraid of her.

I have not gone to the doctor about the problem, because he is under a great deal of stress right now with his critically ill wife. I don't want to give him one more thing to worry about. But my problem is affecting my health. Sometimes my hands tremble, and I get terrible stomach aches just thinking about going to work. I really need to work, and jobs are very hard to find in our rural area. I've even thought about talking to an attorney, but I really don't have the money.

Can you help me figure out what to do?

Desperate RDH

Dear Desperate,

What a sad situation! I'm so sorry you have to deal with such an unpleasant and unfortunate workplace issue.

Your inquiry prompted me to do some research on workplace bullying. Evidently, there is quite a bit of workplace bullying in our society today. In fact, there is an organization called the Workplace Bullying Institute (WBI) that has a wealth of information. (www.workplacebullying.org)

The WBI commissioned Zogby International to conduct a survey and collect data on adult Americans related to workplace bullying. Their research was published in 2010, and here are some key points:

1. 35% of workers have experienced bullying first hand.
2. 62% of bullies are men; 58% of targets are women.
3. Women bullies target women in 80% of cases.
4. Bullying is 4X more prevalent than illegal harassment.
5. The majority (68%) of bullying is same-gender harassment.

I find it interesting that women typically target other women. So much for the YaYa Sisterhood, right? This statistic seems antithetical to the belief that women are nurturers and supporters. According to Gary Namie, PhD, research director with the WBI, the high incidence of women bullying women "is probably some idea that they can find a less confrontative person or someone less likely to respond to aggression with aggression."

The WBI defines bullying as the deliberate, repeated, harmful targeting of another person with disrespectful, insulting, and/or threatening behavior that is intended to be hurtful. This abuse causes the recipient to feel vulnerable, threatened, frightened, and/or humiliated. Bullies may feel jealousy and possess a need to control people. Bullies are not interested in the recipient's feelings and often resort to distortion of the truth. Bullies can use passive-aggressive behaviors to inflict emotional distress on the target by intentionally withholding information or deliberately misinterpreting something the target said to make him/her look bad. Bullying in the workplace is very similar to spousal abuse in the home.

Some of the signs of being the object of bullying in the workplace include trying to avoid being near bullying people, feeling intimidated, lack of communication, muscular tension, and physical illness. You are already experiencing all of these signs.

I consulted in an office that had a bullying staff member. Two different staff members told me about how difficult it was to work with this woman and that many other staff members had left because of her bullying. Although she was good at her job, her presence made the other staff members feel like they were walking on eggshells. The bully was very two-faced, pretending to be congenial to her coworkers in the doctor's presence. Although the doctor had received some complaints about the bully, he was not aware of the seriousness of the problem. The bully was eventually fired, but not before she had caused tremendous damage to the practice.

I believe one of the reasons that bullying has become such a problem in the workplace today is that it is not illegal. There are no laws that prevent bullying. According to the WBI website,

"Bullying certainly looks and feels like harassment. It is harassing, as commonly understood (defined as systematic, annoying, and continued actions which include threats and demands; creating a hostile situation by uninvited and unwelcome verbal or physical conduct). But at work, harassment is a special term. Often, workplace harassment connotes sexual misconduct and a hostile work environment. State and federal civil rights laws are designed to protect workers from discriminatory, disparate mistreatment. If, and ONLY IF, you are a member of a protected status (grounds) group—there are 7 in the U.S. and 11 in Canada—(e.g., gender, race, religion, ethnicity, etc.), and you have been mistreated by a person who is NOT a member of a protected group, you might be able to claim that you were harassed. (Only a legal professional can advise you on this.) HR must respond to your complaint and the entire anti-discrimination procedure begins. Illegal discriminatory harassment occurs in only 20% of bullying cases. That means that 80% of bullying is legal! Bullying is four times more common than either sexual harassment or racial discrimination on the job."

There are some efforts afoot to curb workplace bullying by passing appropriate legislation intended to define the problem and designate remedies for infractions. However, such legislation is still forthcoming.

What should you do? First, you must not delay any longer in informing the doctor of the situation. Do not mince words! You must tell him everything in a very straightforward way. Employers must take seriously their role in providing a safe and non-threatening work environment. Second, start keeping a journal of bullying incidents. Third, if the doctor does not take immediate action, I recommend you request a meeting with the bully in the doctor's presence. Let the doctor and the bullying coworker know that you intend to take further action if the bullying does not end immediately.

Best wishes,

Dianne

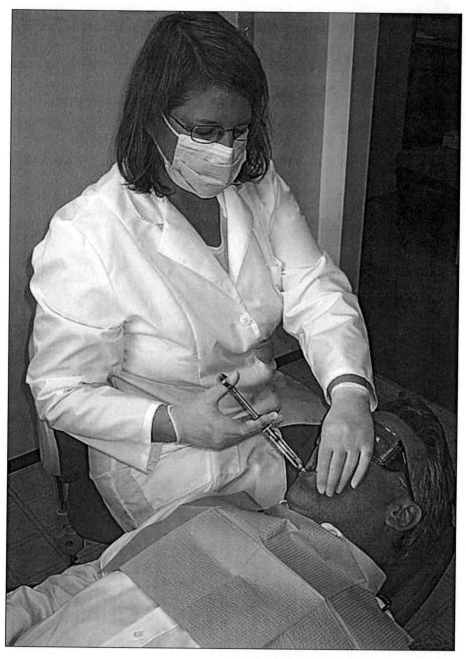

Margaret Fehrenbach, RDH, MS, administering local anesthesia.

The Consummate Dental Hygienist

"Coworker's Speech Habit"

Dear Dianne,

I work with a young lady who has about a 50-word vocabulary, and 49 of the words are 'like.' I literally counted 49 'likes' in a story she was telling the other day. Her 21st birthday is coming up in three weeks, and I have been mulling over something to say to her about her annoying speech habit. Here's what I have been considering:

Me: So, you're, like 21 years old now. Twenty-one is, like, the cutoff age, you know.

Coworker: Cutoff age for, like, what?

Me: For using the word 'like' after every few, like, words in, like, all your, like, sentences.

Does this sound mean? I asked my 22-year-old niece about it, and she said, "One of my friends said that to me in high school, and it only took that one person to make me stop doing it. You should tell her." I thought of another approach that might be a little kinder:

Me: So, do you feel like a real adult now?

Coworker: Oh, yeah!

Me: I've noticed that you still talk like a teenager sometimes.

Coworker: Well, like, whaddaya mean?

Me: You use the word 'like' a lot, sometimes two or three times in one sentence. Since you're 20 now, you should start thinking about the image you project to people.

So, what's your opinion? Should I say something or not?

Annoyed and Anonymous

Dear Annoyed,

I don't know where the inadvertent misuse of the word 'like' came from, but this faddish speech habit has swept the country! It seems everywhere I go, I hear "She was, like, this...", "I was, like, blown away..." "It was, like, craaaazy..." I hear it in airports, malls, gas stations, Walmart, the hospital, and movie theaters. In most cases, the offenders are young females (although males are not immune). My husband and I were in an upscale restaurant, and the woman at the next table was excitedly speaking about something that happened to her at work. As I carefully eavesdropped, I counted 25 'likes' in the space of less than five minutes.

I almost asked the waiter to move us to another table. It seems the word 'like' is being used as a filler word. It has taken the place of 'uh' and in some cases 'you know' except when you are hit with the two-fisted punch: "Like, you know, I was really, like, scared!"

Some people use "Ya-know-what-I-mean" at the end of most of their sentences. My husband spent a weekend with a deer hunting buddy who has that annoying speech habit. Dave came home and showered me with a "ya know what I mean…" I felt my pulse rise and my teeth clench as I warned him if he EVER used that on me again, I was going to shatter the tranquility of our peaceful subdivision by screaming to the top of my lungs!

And what about people who confuse 'imply' and 'infer' or use the non-word 'irregardless.' Another misused word is the pretentious use of the word 'utilize' when the word 'use' will work as well. Or the misuse of the word 'good' when responding to the question "How are you?" By saying "I'm good," the person is saying he is beneficial, kind, favorable, or perhaps virtuous. The correct response is "I'm well, thank you." My son started placing the phrase 'and stuff' at the end of his sentences: "I went to the mall and stuff." My reply was "Did you say you stuffed something, or did you buy some stuff? I hope you weren't shoplifting…" It is an annoying speech habit, and he still does it sometimes!

Please forgive my digression, but you pressed one of my 'hot' buttons. Speech habits are like addictions—they can be very hard to break. Just ask anyone who has broken the habit of saying 'like' every third word, and they will admit the difficulty. One young lady said the only way she could break the habit was when her mother started charging her $1 every time she misused the word 'like.' She used up all her allowance and wound up owing her mother money. The major problem as I see it is this young staff member's poor speech habits reflect negatively on the professionalism of the practice. The young coworker is unaware of how her speech causes others to think she is unintelligent. She probably thinks it is 'hip' and 'preppy' to speak as she does.

Actually, the doctor or office administrator would be the logical person to address this issue. However, knowing the non-confrontational nature of many doctors, it is understandable that the coworker's speech habit has been allowed to persist. If you look at your situation as helping this young, impressionable girl, there's nothing mean-spirited about it. You would be exercising kindness by calling attention to something that casts her in a negative light, but you have to approach it so it does not embarrass her in front of anyone else. "Can I tell you something because I like you a lot and want to help you? You are a sweet, thoughtful person, great assistant (whatever you can say positive about her), but there's a problem maybe you are not aware of..." Both of the examples you suggested are fine, as long as the coworker knows you are trying to help her.

If you refrain from saying anything, the problem will persist until a patient makes a negative comment. Worse still, patients do form negative perceptions about the practice, often without saying anything. Her speech habit is annoying. We, as professionals, should refrain from doing anything that is annoying to our patients.

Akin to this discussion is my recent decision to say something about an irritating, rude situation. My nail technician is from Viet Nam, and he is most excellent. Yesterday I did a slow burn as he carried on a conversation with a coworker in a foreign language the WHOLE time I was in his chair. When he finished, I paid him without tipping. Instead, I motioned for him to step outside the door with me. I said, "Kenny, you do really nice work. Do you like my business?" He looked shocked and surprised but replied that he liked my business. I continued, "Well, today I felt I was treated rudely and disrespectfully by you in being excluded from the ongoing conversation you were having IN A FOREIGN LANGUAGE with your coworker while I was in your chair. If you want my business, please do not ever do that again." He was very apologetic and assured me it would not happen again. I was not trying to be mean-spirited to Kenny; I was trying to help him. I want to give him my business, but I refuse to do business with rude people. How would he know if I did not garner the courage to tell him? Tell your coworker gently as a friend. One day when she has matured, she will appreciate your honesty and kindness.

Best wishes,

Dianne

"Territorialism and Cliques"

Dear Dianne,

For the past 10 years, I have worked in an office with two other hygienists and two doctors. There are three hygiene operatories. One day, my coworker came to me asking if I knew the whereabouts of a particular instrument. Since I didn't have what she was looking for, we went to the other operatory to look. One of the dental assistants saw us in the other operatory searching for the instrument. She told the hygienist who uses that room that she saw us taking things from her room and that she should "watch her back" with me. My coworker called me at home and chewed me out for being in her room.

Now I feel she is trying to sabotage my job. In a strange turn of events, she and the other hygienist have formed a tight clique. They leave me out of everything and have even written notes in patients' charts that are very hurtful about me and questioning the treatment I've recommended for the patient.

I love what I do, and I love my patients who I've been seeing for years now. This tension and struggle has made my confidence as a hygienist decline. There is no unity within the office. It gives me knots in my stomach to think about it and to prepare myself each time I go into work. Never have I had these feelings going into work. It's crazy! I feel sometimes like I'm going into a battlefield. Can you help me sort this out?

Feeling left out

Dear Feeling,

It sounds like there are some serious interpersonal problems that have taken root in your office. No doubt, there is at least one "pot-stirrer" among the bunch. The formation of cliques often leads to gossip and hurt feelings, and the workplace can become toxic.

The first issue that you identified is territorialism. We're kind of like cats, which are highly territorial by nature. If a cat feels she doesn't have proper territory or if she feels that her territory is being encroached upon, aggressive behaviors may ensue. Most hygienists have an assigned operatory and have set up "their" room in a manner that is comfortable to them. We put things in places where we know we can find them, and we don't like it when people come into our space and change things. We don't like it when people take things from our workspace without asking.

You took it upon yourself to help your coworker locate a particular instrument. Did you also make sure she put it back where she found it when she was finished using it? Would you like it if your coworkers took things from your operatory in your absence and didn't return those same items? Maybe the doctor needs to order additional instruments so everyone will have an adequate supply. In most situations, the equipment and instruments belong to the practice, not any particular individual. That doesn't stop us from laying claim on certain items, though.

I do not like sharing instruments. It's best when each hygienist in a practice has his/her own instrument sets and is responsible for keeping them sharp and well maintained. There is great variability among hygienists with regard to sharpening. Instruments can be ruined by hygienists who do not have good sharpening skills. Wars have been known to break out in offices when one hygienist accuses another hygienist of not sharpening correctly.

What disturbs me more than the territorialism is the dental assistant's behavior. Who made her the office police? What was the real reason she chose to create resentment between you and your coworker? Who would have guessed that her little bit of juicy gossip would have caused so much resentment and pain?

Your second issue is the office clique that has formed. Workplace cliques are a near universal reality. All cliques are not negative, as they are a part of natural social interaction. They become problematic when they cause the workplace environment to become stressful and tense. Workplace cliques can and do affect productivity. Cliques that occupy time with gossiping and complaining drain energy from the group. In your situation, it sounds like kindergarten antics where "two's company, three's a crowd." According to an article by Tom Gray, titled "Workplace Cliques: Coping with the Toxic, Joining the Healthy," the way in which you respond to a workplace clique depends on your need to belong. "Not all people require the same degree of social interaction and bonding at work. Some meet their relationship needs mainly outside the workplace; others hope to make plenty of friends on the job. You should look at your own personality to see which type you are."

Clinical notes should not contain opinion or derogatory remarks about any other clinician in the office. The one who records derogatory remarks poses a liability risk to the owner of the practice. For example, if someone writes, "thick, deep calculus at #30 D obviously of long duration," this infers that someone did not do a thorough job in the past. Such inferences increase liability risk. In my opinion, derogatory remarks in the patient chart cross an ethical line that should be addressed directly with the one who recorded the remarks. The questions I would ask are: "What was your purpose in writing this note? Are you trying to discredit me with the doctors? Would you like it if I wrote similar things about the treatment you provide? Are you trying to sabotage my job?"

Your coworkers are acting like children. Here's what you should do. Are you listening? Kill them with kindness. That's right. If you've done nothing wrong, then learn to let this slide. Go to work and do your best for the patients. Be kind and helpful to everyone, even those who have been unkind, and rise above this situation. When you are kind to people, it makes it hard for them to be unkind back. I think this may be why Jesus taught people to "love your enemies." Don't let their antics get you down. *You're a good hygienist.* Think about this. You've been there 10 years. If you were not a good and competent hygienist, do you think you would have kept your job that long? You have some gossipy, pot-stirring coworkers. Vow to NEVER partake of their gossip stew.

And grow a spine. A little direct questioning, unemotional (not in anger or tearfully) confrontation is a way to show your coworkers you want to know if there's a problem you need to correct. "In the future, come directly to me, and please do not sabotage my job. And in return, I'll cut you the same slack. None of us are perfect. If I make a mistake, I want to know about it. And I'll do the same for you. Deal? Thanks, I knew you'd understand."

People can only hurt you to the degree that you allow. Stand up for yourself, and ignore office cliques. You'll be a lot better off!

Best wishes,

Dianne

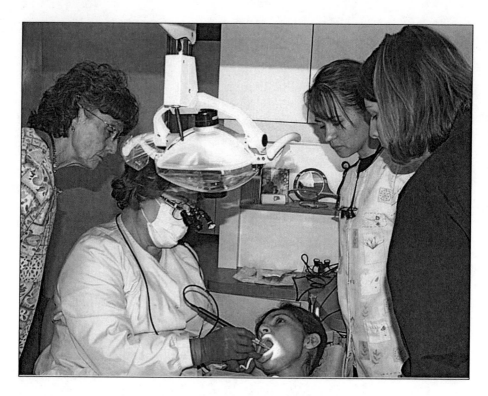

Anne Nugent Guignon, RDH, MPH, teaches a hands-on course.

Chapter 3

Interpersonal Relationships: The Boss

"Spineless Doctor"

Dear Dianne,

I have been a dental hygienist for 15 years, and I have worked full time in the same practice for five years. About three weeks ago, an incident happened in my office that upset me to the point that I am considering giving notice.

The patient was a man who I had seen one other time. I distinctly remembered him from the previous visit. When I seated the patient, he said, "I do not want you to touch my front four teeth, because I'm afraid you will pull my fillings out." I was taken aback by his request, and I asked him if another hygienist had ever dislodged any of his restorations in the past. He replied, "No, but I do not want to take that chance." This is a patient with poor oral hygiene and generalized gingivitis. He would not even allow me to probe the anterior teeth. So when I saw his name on the schedule again, I asked the doctor if he had any ideas on how to approach this problem. He told me to abide by the patient's wishes.

As I seated the patient, he again warned me not to touch his four front teeth in the upper arch. While doing my tour of the mouth, I could see calculus around the gingival margins. I gave the patient a hand mirror and asked him to look with me. When I touched tooth #8 with my explorer, the patient became angry and shouted loudly, "Damn it, I told you not to touch that tooth! Are you deaf?" Everyone in the office heard his angry remark. I was so shocked that I couldn't think of anything to say. I fought back tears.

I completed the rest of the mouth and summoned the doctor. I pointed out to the doctor the gingivitis and calculus at teeth #7-10, and the patient retorted to the doctor, "I told that bitch not to touch those teeth." Guess what the doctor said? Nothing. Absolutely nothing. There was not one word from him in my defense. He finished checking the patient and left the room without a word.

It has been three weeks, and neither of us has broached the subject. Dianne, what, if anything, should I do?

Hurt and angry hygienist

Dear Hurt,

Shame, shame, shame on this doctor for not defending you! At the very least, he should have told the patient, "I will not tolerate your being verbally abusive to my staff member. We're finished here—for good!" Next he should have promptly dismissed this patient from his practice through the appropriate protocol.

First of all, the doctor should have taken the situation by the horns on the patient's previous visit. The patient's admonition to not touch certain teeth was unreasonable and unwarranted. The doctor should have said, "What you have requested is against the law. It is called 'supervised neglect.' We can see visible signs of gum disease, which is completely reversible with conservative care. Since you are so afraid of losing a filling, I will replace—at NO charge to you—any filling that comes loose in the process of a hygiene visit on those four teeth. What do you say?" One would hope the patient would submit under those terms. If the patient still refused care, there would be no argument. The patient would be dismissed from the practice.

However, the patient was allowed to return and verbally harass you without a word from the doctor. I only have one word to describe the doctor's behavior: spineless. I suppose the doctor was so intimidated by the patient's rude and brash behavior that he was speechless. Judging from the previous visit, the doctor should have anticipated unpleasantness from this patient. Indeed, you discussed the previous situation with the doctor, but the doctor declined to take positive action should a similar (or worse) situation arise. A defensive strategy should have been discussed at the morning huddle or before the patient's visit.

Every employer has the responsibility to provide a workplace that is free from harassment, discrimination, and harm. By not taking prompt action in this situation, the doctor did not act within the guidelines set forth by the US Equal Employment Opportunity Commission. The EEOC outlines what constitutes harassment:

Harassment becomes unlawful where 1) enduring the offensive conduct becomes a condition of continued employment, or 2) the conduct is severe or pervasive enough to create a work environment that a reasonable person would consider intimidating, hostile, or abusive. The employer will be liable for harassment by non-supervisory employees or non-employees over whom it has control (e.g., independent contractors or customers on the premises), if it knew, or should have known about the harassment and failed to take prompt and appropriate corrective action. ("http://eeoc.gov/types/harassment.html" http://eeoc.gov/types/harassment.html)

The guidelines go on to say that "isolated incidents (unless extremely serious) will not rise to the level of illegality." However, the latest incident was a second exposure to this patient's unreasonable behavior. Again, this patient relationship should have been terminated after the first appointment if the patient continued his unreasonable behavior.

What should you do? First of all, make sure that the whole incident is thoroughly documented in the patient chart. Put the patient's exact words in quotation marks. Stick to the facts. Next, inform the doctor that if he intends to allow this patient to continue receiving care in the practice, you will not be providing care in the future for this man. Let the doctor know how disappointed you are that he did not rise to your defense. Then ask the doctor if there was anything you said or did that did not meet his expectations.

Some people use verbal rudeness as a control mechanism. They have learned over time that many people are caught off guard or so intimidated by some rude comment or outburst that they do not know how to react quickly. We are not in the habit of receiving verbal abuse, and therefore are unprepared to respond. It is regrettable that your boss did not have the courage to respond appropriately in this unfortunate situation.

Thank goodness, unreasonable patients like the one you described are not common in our practices. I believe most practices have a large majority of people who we enjoy seeing. We often form connected relationships with our patients and become more than a caregiver—we become their friend.

Best wishes,

Diane

"The Pressure Cooker"

Dear Dianne,

I have been a hygienist for five years, but I'm starting to feel like I've chosen the wrong profession. When I came out of school, I was so excited about working as a hygienist and helping people have healthy mouths. I actually loved the clinical challenges of hygiene. Now, I feel disillusioned. The practice where I work is all about production, production, production! The harder I work, the more the doctor pushes. I leave so tired at the end of the day that I need to lie down and rest when I get home before I start preparing dinner for my family. I'm drained physically and emotionally! I need to work, and hygiene jobs are scarce in my area. Is there any way to turn this situation around?

Disillusioned and Defeated

Dear D & D,

Years ago, my mom gave me a pressure cooker as a gift. I learned there are many advantages with pressure cooking, such decreased cooking time and less chance of scorching. I also learned that the heat level under the pot is critical. One day, I filled my pot with water and pinto beans and put my pressure cooker on the stove over high heat. I walked away to do something else, and a few minutes later I heard what sounded like a gunshot then a loud 'whoosh.' Too much sustained heat caused the pressure to build up to the point of popping the safety valve off the lid. The 'whoosh' I heard was the sound of pintos and water spraying all over my ceiling. The lesson I learned that day was never leave a pressure cooker on sustained high heat.

It sounds like you are in a 'pressure cooker' work situation, and the heat is too high. If someone does not turn the heat down, one of these days your safety valve will pop, meaning you will quit suddenly. When that happens, the pressure will be relieved, but it may leave a mess for you and your employer to clean up.

All pressure cooker work situations are not bad. In the pressure cooker, we learn to work efficiently and not waste time. We develop strength of character and perseverance. We develop systems and problem-solve situations so that we can be effective at our jobs.

However, I also learned that if you leave something in the pressure cooker too long, it cooks to mush. The food is ruined and has to be thrown out. Too much time in the work pressure cooker can make people develop 'unpalatable' attitudes, such as indifference, disillusionment, and chronic discontent. These negative attitudes affect how we interact with each other and our patients.

If we could describe the ideal practice, it would have these aspects:

- Sufficient time to deliver high-quality care

- Great equipment and instruments

- Patients who show up and appreciate our care

- Bosses who appreciate us and our contribution to the practice

- Coworkers who function as a team

Unfortunately, ideal practices are few and far between. My experience is that staff members will adapt to most any practice situation if they feel loved and appreciated. There are doctors who have mastered the most difficult clinical techniques and have spent thousands of dollars on technology and education, yet they have never learned what makes an effective leader in their practices, beginning with expressing sincere appreciation to their staff members. They have never learned that the heat has to be carefully controlled under the pressure cooker. In addition, doctors who are so money driven that they turn the focus from excellent patient care to achieving some arbitrary daily number are not aware of the damage they do to staff morale. Staff members lose respect for doctors like that. Staff turnover costs the practice significant amounts of money as well.

Please understand production IS important. If the practice is not producing adequately, it cannot pay its debts, which includes staff salaries. The current economic hard times will affect all businesses, and those practices with significant debt will suffer most. Who knows? The doctor you work with may be worried about keeping the practice solvent, which may explain the preoccupation with production.

Since you stated leaving is not an option, my advice is for you to change the way you view your job by being thankful every workday that you have a job. Demonstrate excellent care to the patients by doing your best, and look for ways to work efficiently. Treat your patients and co-workers with kindness and compassion, and remember why you are there in the first place. Make the doctor glad to have you as a team member. A good attitude will help you control the heat in your particular pressure cooker situation. Lastly, try to avoid the negative feelings that come from the doctor's preoccupation with production.

Life is full of pressure cooker situations. Whether we like it or not, every one of us will be in the pressure cooker at some time or other. Whether pressure situations make us bitter or better depends on how we respond to the challenge. We cannot change people, but we can change how we respond to pressures by developing the positive attitudes we need to help us cope.

Best wishes,

Dianne

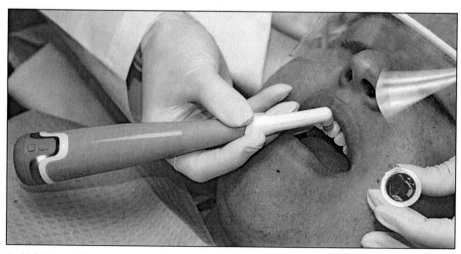

Polishing with a cordless device.

"Unorthodox Periodontal Protocol"

Dear Dianne,

I have practiced dental hygiene for more than 20 years and have been employed at one particular office for more than 15 years. Four years ago, I accepted an additional part-time position to help bolster my finances. Both practices are similar in that they serve primarily blue-collar clientele. I consider the long-term position my primary position and the shorter term my secondary position. I have always known that my long-time boss has "control" issues and rarely delegates anything. For example, he insists on making all of his own temporary crowns and uses his assistant only for suction, instrument/material passing, and clean-up, even though she is qualified to perform many other procedures.

Now that I am employed in two offices, I see two different levels of care being given to patients. In the secondary office, I am expected to do a full periodontal charting every year; a full review of medical history every recall; a complete intraoral and head-and-neck cancer exam every recall; and create a treatment plan for scaling/root planing when signs of active periodontal disease are present.

The standards are less defined in my primary position. My primary employer and I have butted heads in the past regarding periodontal treatment. When periodontal pockets exceed 5 mm, he treats the pockets in his operatory with a gingivectomy performed with an electrosurgery cauterizing unit and his own root planing performed with a single posterior scaler. He rarely allows me to perform SRP by quadrant or even localized. I know this a loaded question, but are his treatment methods below the medico-legal standard of care for treating chronic periodontal diseases? I do not ask this question to punish him in any way, but I am concerned for my license and the care of the patients. Can you help me?

Stacey

Dear Stacey,

I have been in dentistry since 1972, and never have I heard of anyone treating periodontal disease in the unorthodox manner you described.

I posed your question to several doctors, and here are a few of their replies:

"Apparently the doctor you are describing is a sad dysfunctional dentist story, bilking money with ridiculous treatment. I would suggest this hygienist seek employment elsewhere, and then blow the whistle on this incompetent."

"This clinician could be sued for malpractice."

"Put in cold steel and phenol, and you have 1925 dentistry. This is not good in my mind. Leaves a BIG defect and other nasty things... Better post-treatment aesthetics IS important to most patients."

"The word 'cowboy' comes to mind, in the bad connotation. I feel sorry for the dentist's patients, because they have no clue about the effectiveness of what he is doing or the ethics involved. Does this dentist ever refer to a periodontist?"

"It causes severe gingival recession. This practice is historical as far as I know."

The standard of care is defined as what other reasonable and prudent practitioners do in a similar circumstance. Furthermore, if a practitioner engages in care that is typically thought of as "specialty care," he or she usually must meet the same standard of care required of the specialist. Therefore, it is safe to say that routinely treating periodontitis with gingivectomies is outside the current standard of care.

I could comment on the doctor's lack of business acumen as well. Not delegating to his qualified chairside assistant is a wasteful use of her skills. Further, it is common knowledge that non-surgical treatment of periodontal disease is the most productive procedure a hygienist performs. If the doctor insists on doing all the periodontal treatment, he is under-utilizing his well-trained hygienists. What is he thinking??!!

Business acumen aside, the most important issue at stake here is patient care. These words of wisdom are from Michael Rethman, DDS, past president of the American Academy of Periodontology:

"In my opinion, what's described here does NOT jibe with what the standard of care is for mild to moderate chronic periodontitis. Ideally, highly competent ScRP ought to be attempted at each periodontitis site at least once and each site re-assessed before considering more aggressive approaches. This is because despite the fact that shallow probing depths are generally nicer to have than deep probing depths, the fundamental goal of such therapy is to eliminate the cause of the infection (and keep it eliminated via self-care and maintenance). Most times, non-surgical approaches, especially when performed by experts (who may also be using the added advantage of perioscopy) followed up by high-quality self-care and routine professional maintenance will work just fine at such sites, despite whatever probing depths remain. Surgery generally makes the most sense when non-surgical approaches have failed to achieve health. Gingivectomies are seldom appropriate other than for suprabony pocketing. Furthermore, gingivectomies are most often used to remove excess gingiva that is coronal to the cemento-enamel junction."

It would seem that the doctor's use of gingivectomy may be based in some historical protocol. However, we are more knowledgeable today about effective treatments for periodontal disease than at any time in the past. Every clinician has the burden, by virtue of being licensed by his/her state licensing board, to stay current with treatment protocols. That is why continuing education is mandated throughout the country. The result of not staying current regarding treatment protocols brings about an undesirable treatment outcome and a possible danger to the patient. The liability risk is high for the doctor if a patient ever decides to sue for malpractice related to his unorthodox treatment. As a hygienist, you are also at some theoretical risk, although I don't know of a situation similar to this when a hygienist has been sued.

At the other end of the spectrum are those clinicians who espouse new and emerging treatment protocols that are untested and largely unproven by unbiased sources. They risk liability as well. When a new treatment is advertised as a 'profit center' for the practice, I get an uneasy feeling. The goal of any 'new' treatment modality should be to enhance/improve the care we provide for those people who place their trust in us and our abilities, not lighten their bank account. If a patient decides to sue a clinician for malpractice related to a treatment outcome involving 'novel' treatments, the clinician could be charged with practicing outside the standard of care. It could be that the care delivered is not the currently accepted standard of care.

It is unfortunate that your employer has not stayed current and is treating unknowing patients with incorrect, unethical treatment that causes pain and unaesthetic results. Whether you should continue to work in his practice will require some soul searching. If I was in your position, I would probably leave.

Best wishes,

Dianne

The author with Mary Moran Bodreau and Judith Dember-Paige.

"Supervised Neglect"

Dear Dianne,

I've been in dental hygiene for more than 25 years, and during that time, I have worked for several dentists. Two of my former employers were outstanding clinicians who took great pride in the dentistry they provided. The majority were just average dentists. However, my current boss is practicing what I believe to be supervised neglect.

When I took the position six months ago, I had no idea what I was getting into. Many, if not most, patients have never had a periodontal charting—ever! I have seen many substandard crowns with excessive margins and decay. I have witnessed decay on bite wings that the doctor says to 'watch.' When I detect periodontal disease, the doctor tells me to just do a prophy. Recently, when I told the doctor I could not do a prophy because the patient had overt periodontal disease, she fired me. Then she called and begged me to come back. The day she fired me, she closed the office down and sent everyone home.

The doctor accepts capitation plans, which means she gets money from insurance companies whether she does any dentistry or not. While I'm not sure how capitation affects the dentistry, I'm seeing a 'dark side' of dentistry that I never knew existed. Believe me, I would leave this practice in a heartbeat, but jobs are scarce in my area. I have bills to pay and a family to support.

I am very concerned about the patients, but I am also concerned about my license. I believe this doctor needs a mental health evaluation. I have considered reporting her to the state board, because I believe she is practicing below the current standard of care. What are the implications if I report her?

No Name Please

Dear No Name,

As you are aware, state boards are charged with ensuring that the standards of care of dentistry are not violated. State boards are in place to protect the public. But what are "standards of care?"

Simply put, standards of care are those standards that are taught in accredited schools of dentistry and dental hygiene and are practiced by members of the profession. In 1898, there was a landmark case that set forth what "standard of care" entails. To summarize, the court stated that a doctor must:

Possess a reasonable degree of learning and skill that is ordinarily possessed by clinicians in the same locality.

Use reasonable care and diligence in the exercise of skill.

Keep up with the latest advances in the profession. Use the clinician's best judgment in exercising skill and applying knowledge.

Exercise the skill and learning possessed by the average member of the profession in good standing, not necessarily of the best practitioner.

Use approved methods in general use.

Give proper instruction to the patient (Pollack, 2002).

In judging whether a professional has been negligent, the courts use a standard called the reasonable prudent person or professional. This means the court compares what a reasonably prudent person or professional would have done in a similar situation. Thus, maintaining a practice that meets or exceeds the standard of care is extremely important for dental hygienists. Failure to include a procedure or step in treatment because the clinician claims to be unaware of the current standard will not hold up in court.

You mentioned the absence of periodontal charting. This is a serious violation of the standard of care. It is generally accepted that the standard is every adult patient receives a six-point probing at a minimum of once per year. It is likely that periodontal disease has gone undetected in the practice.

Because of the nature of the work, hygienists are in a good position to evaluate the quality of the doctor's work up close. From your letter, it sounds like the doctor may not be practicing to the established standards of care regarding restorative dentistry if you are seeing numerous carious lesions that are not being addressed.

You also mentioned that the doctor is on several capitation plans. Capitation plans pay doctors a set amount of money per month to see covered patients, and 'cap' doctors are supposed to provide whatever dentistry is needed by the patient. Doctors who sign on get the capitation payment whether they see one or 100 capitation patients. In that regard, it seems like a disincentive to treat, in my opinion. An interesting article was published in the *British Dental Journal* in March, 1990, titled "The capitation study. Does capitation encourage 'supervised neglect'?" This was the conclusive statement in the study: "Dentists in capitation carried out fewer fillings, fewer extractions, took fewer radiographs and saw their patients less frequently than their fee-for-service colleagues."

There are several things you need to consider. First, you mentioned the doctor's abrasive treatment toward you. Here's my question: If the doctor had treated you well, would you still be considering reporting her to the state board? I'm not excusing the doctor's obvious lack of tact and respect, but everyone goes through rough places in their lives from time to time.

Second, if you report her, she could lose her license, which may or may not be in the best interest of patient care. The residual outcome would be you would lose your job. Your license would not be in jeopardy as long as your chart notes accurately reflect what you observed in the patient's mouth and your care was at or above the accepted standards of care.

Third, unless your state board allows 'anonymous' reporting, you could be labeled as a 'whistle-blower' which could affect your ability to work in your area. You could be the finest hygienist in the world, but if no one will hire you, you cannot use those skills that you have perfected over the years.

Can this situation have a happy ending? Only time will tell. You are in a position to help her if she will allow your assistance. Consider how you might be able to help this doctor bring her practice up to the established standards of care.

Otherwise, I see major trouble. My mom says, "If you give a dog enough rope, he'll eventually hang himself," which means if a dog is on a long enough leash, he will run around in various directions until he wraps the rope around a tree or other obstacles in his path and cause his own demise by choking. The application is that sooner or later, this doctor will be sued for substandard care IF she doesn't change her ways. In the meantime, try to help her if you can during your search for a new practice home. You have a BIG challenge!

Best wishes,

Dianne

References: Holloway, PJ, Lennon, MA, Mellor, AC, Coventry, P, Worthington, HV. (1990). *The capitation study. Does capitation encourage 'supervised neglect'?* British Dental Journal, Volume 168, No. 3, 119-121. Pollack, B. (2002). *Law and Risk Management in Dental Practice.* Carol Stream, IL: Quintessence.

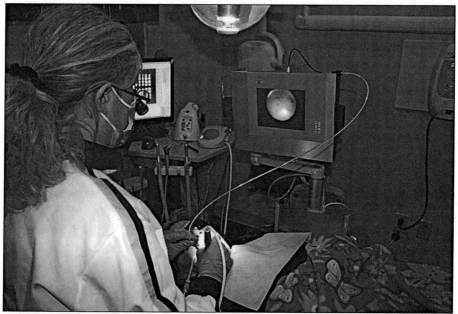

Judy Carroll, RDH, working with her dental endoscope.

Chapter 4

Clinical Issues

Besides "getting along" with our patients and helping them to feel comfortable, we must also provide the dental services for which they came to see us. This may seem a straightforward task, but it can be fraught with uncertainties, questions, and problems. This section will focus on the problems often faced by clinical hygienists in the course of a typical workday, and provide solutions that have proven to be effective and beneficial.

"I Hate Probing"

Dear Dianne,

OK, I'll admit it—I hate probing! It is the only part of my job that I truly hate. There are several reasons why I hate probing. First, I don't have enough time. It takes me anywhere from 10-15 minutes to chart a full dentition by myself, yet I'm only given 40 minutes for the average prophy patient. Second, there's no one to help me get all the numbers written down, and I have to contaminate the patient chart to get everything recorded. Third, I don't like making my patients uncomfortable, and probing hurts. Fourth, there are areas of the mouth where I can't see the probe, such as linguals of posterior teeth. Fifth, it seems like such a pointless exercise, since the doctor never looks at the chart anyway.

With all these objections, it is easy to see why I hate probing. I know I should be perio charting my patients, and I feel guilty that I'm not doing something I know I should do. Help!

Guilty RDH

Dear Guilty,

I like your honesty, and I'm glad you are feeling guilty about not probing. Recognition of a problem is the first step in finding solutions for the obstacles you expressed so succinctly. Let's examine each issue, starting with a lack of time.

It sounds like you work in a high-volume office if you are given only 40 minutes on average with your patients. You have to prioritize and use every minute wisely. Hygienists who work in these situations often do just what I used to do when I was time pressed, which was performing a "drive-by" probing. I'd probe here and there and write in the chart notes "Probing WNL" which was supposed to mean "within normal limits" but could easily mean "we never looked." Those "drive-by" probing charts that only have a number here and there appear—to a jury of non-dental people—to be incomplete. Remember this: In a court of law, if it's not written in the chart, it never happened.

I distinctly remember a patient who expressed discomfort near a mandibular second molar when the doctor did the hygiene exam. The doctor discovered an 8 mm pocket at the DL that I completely missed. I felt terrible! The reason I missed it was because I wasn't looking for it. I had not performed a thorough periodontal assessment of my patient. That was a wake-up call for me. I accepted the blame for missing the pocket, but the doctor had to accept blame for not giving me sufficient time to perform that all-important charting. When the office hired an assistant to help all five hygienists in our office perform comprehensive probings, we discovered many periodontal problems on our patients that we had previously missed. The discovery led to more definitive periodontal treatment, which led to higher production overall.

For your time issue, here's what I recommend. Try to be proactive with scheduling. What I mean is to think ahead and determine what will be needed at the next appointment. If you know the patient will need a full-mouth periodontal charting at the next recall visit, schedule accordingly by allowing an extra 10 minutes. Use the exam code D0180 and charge a higher fee than you charge for a D0120 periodic exam. This will cover the expense of the additional time required to do what is necessary.

The second problem you mentioned was not having assistance. There's nothing better than having an additional person present to record what you find either in the computer or in the paper chart. If the doctor has only one chairside assistant, it is doubtful she would be available when you need her. However, there are several alternatives that you should explore. The first one I want you to check out is something called

PerioPal™ (periopal.com). In essence, it is a voice-command program that allows you to speak what you see through the use of a headset that is plugged into your computer. It was invented by a practicing hygienist who saw the need for a viable option for assistance while probing. This program is like a "super assistant!" All you have to do is learn the commands, and the program does all the charting work. PerioPal is miles beyond the old voice-recognition systems, in that this program responds to commands. The commands are logical and easy to learn. It allows the hygienist to keep eyes focused on the oral cavity and complete probing without having to interrupt the sequence.

Another option is called the Dental R.A.T.™, which stands for "remote access terminal." It is, in essence, a foot-controlled mouse. Also invented by a hygienist, this device allows the hygienist to probe and record the readings with the foot. It is an ingenious invention that allows periodontal charting solo without having to break sequence by stopping to record. The learning curve is not difficult. It's a matter of learning to depress the appropriate position on the foot-activated mouse. (dentalrat.com)

Periodontal probing should not be an unpleasant experience for your patient unless the tissue is inflamed or your technique is heavy handed. If the tissue is inflamed and sore, using a small amount of topical anesthetic in the sulcus will help to alleviate discomfort. Two good topicals that can be squirted in the sulcus are Ultracare (Ultradent®) or Cetacaine (Beutlich®). I also feel that plastic-tipped probes are generally more comfortable than metal probes, especially if there are hypersensitive root surfaces. Now, if you are applying too much pressure, you need to be intentional about reducing your pressure so you don't punch through the crest of the attachment into the connective tissue.

Your inability to see the probe's depth markings is strong evidence that you need magnification. In fact, I will emphatically state that every practicing hygienist should be wearing magnification. Hygienists who do not wear magnification are not aware of what they are missing. Magnification also helps the hygienist's posture by negating the need to bend and crane the neck and back. Designs for Vision® (designsforvision.com) provides excellent vision-enhancing products (loupes and headlights) for dental professionals. Located in Ronkonkoma, N.Y., their products are made and assembled 100% in the U.S., unlike any of their competitors. Their quality and customer service are top notch. You can call their headquarters and they will send a rep to your office to obtain the measurements that are needed and allow you to choose your frames. They also have a 45-day, money-back guarantee. And while you're at it, check out their new "mini" headlight that is powerful, yet small and lightweight.

Periodontal charting is a part of your professional obligation in providing high-quality care. Doctors depend on hygienists to keep them informed about the patient's periodontal status. You should have a full-mouth, six-point periodontal charting for every adult patient once per year, and spot probings of problem areas at interim visits. Every time you chart, you should show the charting to the doctor before he or she examines the patient and point out any areas of concern. Omission of the periodontal charting leaves the doctor open to liability for failure to diagnose periodontal disease. If you implement the recommendations I've shared with you, I think you will overcome your distaste for periodontal charting.

Best wishes,

Dianne

Dear Dianne,

*I work in a busy one-doctor pr*a[...]
is booked very tightly, and it is no[...]
We get 40 minutes for the average p[...]
tal patients.

I know periodontal probing is important, [...]
periodontal probing into a 40-minute appoi[...]
a few marked areas and write "WNL" (within[...]
However, to do a full periodontal probing and re[...]
consuming. Really, the only time I have time to do t[...]
periodontal patient. My question is this: Are my chart[...]
What is the standard of care related to probing and reco[...]
readings?

F[...]

Dear Feeling,

I think you already know the answer to your question. That's why yo[...]
are 'feeling worried.' The standard of care is generally defined as the leve[...]
of care provided by the majority of practitioners in the same field. However, we must also consider the concept of "prudent practice" which
includes "methods taught in dental/dental hygiene schools, continuing
education courses, and/or covered in articles" (Hodges, 1998). Courts
have been known to hold practitioners to the same standards as specialists
when patients have not been referred.

Certainly, the periodontal charting is an important part of diagnosis of
periodontal disease. However, many hygienists think of the periodontal
charting as a burdensome part of their average day and find it easy to
omit. Hodges (1998), quoting McCullough, relates a study published in
the *Journal of Periodontology* that "showed that out of 2,488 records
chosen at random in 36 dental practices, only 16 percent were complete
or adequate in regard to periodontal information" (p. 524). In my chart
audits in dental practices, I have observed a similar situation. In one
recent practice, out of 30 adult charts I pulled at random from the
patient files, only two had an up-to-date periodontal charting.

ns
their
pprise
nsibil-
erious
in
with

as

r

tice with two other hygienists. Our schedule
uncommon for us to run behind schedule.
ophy patient and one hour for periodon-

out it is very difficult to work
tment. Most of the time, I check
normal limits) in the chart.
ord all the numbers is time
hat is when I have a
notations sufficient?
ding of probe

ling Worried

... have

help regarding

... perform this task efficiently if

...ord the numbers. Therefore, I'd like to ask each

...up when you can. Not having an up-to-date charting puts us in a potentially serious situation legally, and if I get sued, it could affect your jobs." I think this puts the situation in perspective.

Three full-time hygienists mean approximately 30 patients to check throughout the day for one doctor, which is, no doubt, a daunting task. If you presently have only one assistant, she is probably maxed out time wise assisting the doctor. Depending on how many chairside assistants there are in the practice, this may be a good time to hire an additional assistant to help with chartings and other various clinical duties. Some offices use business assistants as well to help record periodontal charting numbers.

Another suggestion for you is to be proactive in scheduling, which means when you know your patient will be due for a full-mouth probing on the next visit, allow more time in the schedule for that to happen. An extra 10 minutes can make all the difference in whether the probing is done or not. I agree that 40 minutes is insufficient time for performing all the assessments that are vitally important in providing competent care and perform a thorough prophylaxis.

An important side benefit of full probing on a regular basis is that you will discover more periodontal disease. Non-surgical treatment of periodontal disease is the most productive procedure a hygienist performs. So, it follows that your production will increase as you detect periodontal disease and schedule treatment. You cannot treat it until it is diagnosed, and periodontal probing is the way it is detected.

It is important to communicate your concerns to the doctor. When s/he understands the implications of your dilemma, the solution will be evident. You need a little extra time and someone to help record readings, or purchase a voice-activated system.

Best wishes,

Dianne

Reference: Hodges, Kathleen. (1998). Concepts in Nonsurgical Periodontal Therapy. Albany, NY: Delmar Publishing.

Dr. David Drummond and staff members.

"The Blood and Guts Hygienist"
(letter from a dentist)

Dear Dianne,

I have a hygienist who has been working in my office for nearly a year. She is very conscientious and dedicated to her work, but the problem is that she hurts people. Several patients have complained to me about their uncomfortable hygiene visit. My previous hygienist was with me for 20 years, and I don't recall one patient ever complaining about her causing pain. This situation is a matter of concern to me, and I do not want people to leave my practice because of pain in the hygiene chair. How is the best way to deal with this situation? Do you have any tips to offer?

Concerned Doc

Dear Concerned,

The one thing we know for sure is this: People do not like to go to the dentist! Nearly 40 million people avoid the dentist, according to Dr. James K. Bahcall, a Chicago-based endodontist and author of "Smile for Life: A Guide to Overcoming Your Fear of the Dentist" (Avalon Lane Publishing). Pain is the most often cited reason. In a 2003 survey conducted by the American Dental Association, more than 21% of people cited "fear of pain" as their reason why they avoid routine care.

People who are 'phobic' about going to the dentist have an expectation of pain. They know dental procedures involve needles and sharp, scary-looking tools. I tell my audiences all the time that if clinicians hurt patients, especially on the first visit, they are living down to the patient's expectations, and the patient will have an even more difficult time returning. This issue of pain in the dental office is responsible for many broken/cancelled appointments.

If a patient has a healthy periodontium, preventive care should not cause pain. Yet some clinicians develop heavy-handed instrumentation techniques that tear the epithelial attachment and sulcular epithelium in the process of debridement. Periodontal probing can also cause pain if the clinician uses excessive pressure with the probe. A study by Garnick and Silverstein (*J Periodontol.* Jan. 2000) demonstrated that probe force can cause the probe to penetrate the junctional epithelium, especially if the patient has periodontal disease. Ouch!

Most likely, your hygienist is not aware that she is being unduly rough. I do not believe hygienists 'like' to cause pain, but rather accept the fact that it is sometimes necessary to get the job done.

However, if five patients relate a problem to you, you can bet many more feel the same way but just have not expressed the problem to you. Sometimes people find it easier to go elsewhere for care rather than vocalize their issues with either you or a staff member.

First, I would advise you to experience her care personally by being her patient. You may be able to ascertain why patients are complaining.

Second, it is imperative that you speak with your hygienist about this problem. I would approach it privately by using real examples. "Carol, there's something we need to discuss and work out before it becomes a big negative to us here. Over the past few months, several patients have voiced to me that their preventive care was painful. These are patients who have not had issues in the past. Tell me, have you noticed this becoming a problem? When a patient expresses pain, what do you do?" This gives your hygienist a chance to speak. It is hoped she will accept the discussion as an opportunity to improve her treatment. After all, how can she improve if she does not know there is a problem?

Next, please make available any number of alternatives for short-term anesthesia, such as Oraqix® (Dentsply), HurriPAK® (Cetylite), or UltraCare® (UltraDent). These anesthetics can be squirted into the sulcus to give short-term anesthesia in tender tissues. Make your hygienist aware that patient comfort is important to you, and you want to do everything you can to help her have the same goal.

Years ago, I took a position in an office when the previous hygienist relocated to a different city. Patients made comments like, "You didn't hurt me like the other hygienist." One patient told me that he got so tired of "having my gums ripped to shreds" that he decided to go to another practice. Imagine his shock when the same hygienist summoned him to the treatment area in the second practice—he did not know she worked two days per week in that practice as well! He called her "The old blood and guts hygienist."

People with inflamed tissues are more likely to experience pain than healthy patients. Make sure your hygienist is using local anesthesia appropriately when scaling periodontal patients. If your state does not allow hygienists to administer anesthesia, show her your willingness to provide that service for any patient who needs it. I mention this because I have observed hygienists trying to perform periodontal scaling without anesthesia, usually because they do not want to waste time waiting on the doctor to come and deliver the anesthetic. If your hygienist can administer anesthesia, make sure she is using the proper low-pain technique in delivery.

Once you make her aware there is a problem, it is up to her to make the necessary adjustments. Set a time to meet again in one month to assess progress toward resolution. Make sure to keep track of any further patient complaints. The goal would be zero patient complaints.

Best wishes,

Dianne

David Watterson, Cathy Seckman, RDH, Randy Seckman, and Dianne Watterson on the C & O Canal in Maryland in the Washington, D.C., area.

The Consummate Dental Hygienist

"Periodontal Maintenance Forever?"

Dear Dianne,

I have a patient who went through root planing/scaling and has been on periodontal maintenance for the last 10 years (D4910). His probing depths are all within normal limits at 2-3 mm with no bleeding on probing. He has recession which has been stable since I have been treating him. He comes in every six months. His wife called and was very upset with our coding because the insurance does not cover periodontal maintenance procedures at 100% like they would if we just used a prophylaxis code (D1110). Our office has two dentists who are recent graduates and six hygienists. We need to be on the same page concerning this issue. Could you give us any advice on this matter?

Christy

Dear Christy,

You have posed a great question, one that many hygienists struggle with regularly. I think the initial confusion centered on the strict wording of code D4910 which contains the phrase "for the life of the dentition." Many people took the phrase quite literally and proclaimed "once a periodontal patient, always a periodontal patient." That phrase is true, in the sense that periodontal disease is chronic and must be controlled. However, due to concerns expressed by clinicians to the ADA CDT Code Committee, a clarifying statement was added to give practicing dentists the discretion to judge how a given patient may be maintained. Here is the statement:

"This is a matter of clinical judgment by the treating dentist. Follow-up patients who have received active periodontal therapy (surgical or non-surgical) are appropriately reported using the periodontal maintenance code D4910. However, if the treating dentist determines that a patient's oral condition can be treated with a routine prophylaxis, delivery of this service and reporting with code D1110 may be appropriate."

So what they are saying is 'yes,' some people can be maintained with a prophylaxis. I think we have all seen periodontal patients who previously had periodontal disease, had it treated successfully, and get to a point where they have **no signs of active disease over time.** Such patients can be maintained with a prophylaxis.

Take the patient in your example. You stated he has been stable for a number of years on six-month recare cycles. By 'stable,' you mean he has no continuing loss of attachment or supporting bone and no signs of active disease. If that gentleman moved to a different city and went to a dental office as a new patient where, upon examination, they saw no signs of active disease, how would they treat him? Most likely, this gentleman would get a prophylaxis.

Carrying this example further, let's say the doctor decides this patient can be maintained with a prophylaxis. Two years later, what if the patient starts to exhibit signs of disease again—bleeding on probing, inflammation, increased pocket depths? Then the patient has to have definitive periodontal treatment again and will need periodontal maintenance (D4910) for a period of time until stability returns. If the patient never gets to that stable point, he will need to be maintained with periodontal maintenance indefinitely.

What is the difference between a prophylaxis and periodontal maintenance? A prophylaxis is **preventive** in nature and includes "removal of plaque, calculus, and stains from the tooth structures in the permanent and transitional dentition. It is intended to control local irritational factors." Said differently, a prophylaxis is for people who may have gingivitis but no signs of active periodontal disease. Periodontal maintenance is **therapeutic** in nature and includes "removal of bacterial plaque and calculus from supragingival and subgingival regions, site-specific scaling and root planing where indicated, and polishing the teeth." Periodontal maintenance should always follow definitive periodontal therapy for a period of time, typically one year or longer. I advocate the extensive use of power scalers with thin inserts that are effective in reaching the depths of periodontal pockets for thorough debridement, touching every square millimeter of root surface multiple times, in addition to hand scaling where needed.

One thing that makes our work so interesting is that there is so much variation among our patients with regard to their ability to fight off and control disease. Host defense is not a static entity but fluctuates over a lifetime. Systemic diseases and stress have the ability to cause fluctuations in host resistance, which can cause changes in periodontal health. One patient may get along well for several years. Then suddenly, things start to go downhill periodontally. Sometimes we can pinpoint reasons for such regression, but many times the reason eludes us. People have many variations related to the host and how able it is to fight off disease. Certainly, the patient's home care is important, but people with established periodontal disease cannot stop or control their periodontal problem without good professional care. Conversely, we have all seen people with terrible oral hygiene who do not progress into periodontal disease, such as old Mr. Jones. He comes in every appointment looking like he has brushed his teeth with a doughnut, yet he does not have periodontitis.

One other caveat I should mention is that some insurance companies have instituted new guidelines that they will only pay on D4910 for a period of time, such as two years. One example is United Healthcare. Under pressure from insurance companies and patients, some practices might feel compelled to revert to D1110 in those circumstances. Beware! Let me be clear that *all clinicians have legal and ethical obligations to bill accurately for what they do.* If the procedure provided for the patient is a periodontal maintenance procedure, you must bill D4910, regardless whether the patient's benefits will cover the procedure or not. If a patient receives a prophylaxis, the correct billing code is D1110. (This was covered in the July/August 2008 issue of *Insurance Solutions Newsletter,* www.dental-ins-solutions.com).

Patients are usually happy when we feel they have made such good progress that they can be maintained with a prophylaxis. Typically, it is the dental hygienist who monitors the patient's progress closely, and based on the patient's clinical outcome over time, recommends to the doctor what s/he feels is appropriate treatment for the near future. The decision is very important to the patient's long-term success and should be decided individually, based on stability or the ongoing signs of active disease.

Further, it is inappropriate to alternate between code D1110 and D4910, as the former code is reserved for patients who do not exhibit signs of periodontal disease.

How can a person be disease free one visit, then three months later need periodontal maintenance, then three months later be disease free again? Keep in mind the nature of the procedures as stated previously—one is preventive, one is therapeutic.

I hope this helps to get everyone in your office calibrated concerning periodontal maintenance. Thanks for spotlighting this important issue!

Best wishes,

Dianne

"Codes D1110 & D4910—What's the Difference?"

Why Is It So Hard to Explain to Patients?

By Dianne Glasscoe Watterson and Bill Landers

You have completed a series of definitive periodontal scaling visits with your patient. The next step is periodontal maintenance, which will entail the patient returning every three months. After two visits, the patient learns that he's being charged more for his maintenance visits than his spouse's preventive visits and wants to know why.

The Necessity for Maintenance

Many patients resist regular periodontal maintenance visits after a definitive periodontal scaling. One reason is the higher fee charged for a D4910 periodontal maintenance than the fee for D1110 prophylaxis. The other reason is that most third-party payers do not cover care at three-month intervals.

There is clear evidence for the necessity of a season of maintenance. Periodontal pathogens can entirely repopulate previously scaled teeth in as little as 9-11 weeks. The majority of periodontal patients are not able to debride the depths of periodontal pockets with self-care measures alone. In fact, a position paper published in September 2003 by the American Academy of Periodontology states that "tooth loss in periodontal patients is inversely proportional to the frequency of professional care." Following a 10-year study, the researchers found that patients who had undergone regular periodontal maintenance had significantly reduced probing depths and lost fewer teeth than patients who did not have periodontal maintenance procedures. These are logical arguments for the necessity of maintenance.

However, many hygienists perform exactly the same procedures for a prophylaxis as they do for periodontal maintenance. It's only natural for patients to balk at paying higher fees when there doesn't seem to be any difference between a periodontal maintenance appointment and a prophylaxis appointment.

"What we have here is a failure to communicate."

(Cool Hand Luke, 1967)

Some hygienists themselves don't understand that there indeed are important differences between a periodontal maintenance procedure and a regular prophylaxis. Others understand the difference but have trouble explaining it to their patients.

What Makes the Codes Different?

The D1110 prophylaxis is only for people who do not exhibit any of the signs and symptoms of periodontal disease, including bone loss, bleeding, mobility, exudate, and recession. D1110 is thus a preventive procedure for patients who don't yet have periodontal disease and should only be used with patients who are periodontally healthy. As the CDT definition says, D1110 is for "the removal of plaque, calculus and stains from the tooth structures in the permanent and transitional dentition. It is intended to control local irritational factors."

The D4910 code, on the other hand, is a post-therapeutic procedure used to maintain the results of periodontal therapy, not to prevent disease in healthy patients. The CDT definition for D4910 states that it can only be used: *"following periodontal therapy and continues at varying intervals ... includes removal of the bacterial plaque and calculus from supragingival and subgingival regions, site-specific scaling and root planing where indicated, and polishing the teeth."*

The D4910 code is to be used following definitive perio therapy for an indefinite time, determined by the patient's progress over time to achieve stability and the absence of the signs and symptoms of disease. Some patients have great success after a year or two of definitive maintenance and reach a point where they have no signs or symptoms of active disease, i.e., little if any bleeding on probing and no continuing loss of bone or attachment. Patients in this category do not smoke and have very good-to-excellent oral hygiene. Other patients never get to the point of having no signs and symptoms of disease. Maintenance patients who have poor OH, smoke, and continue to exhibit bone loss and/or excessive bleeding have not achieved an acceptable level of stability and good health. Such patients should be seen by a periodontist and may need D4910 maintenance indefinitely after definitive treatment.

What are the specific differences between a periodontal maintenance procedure vs. a regular prophylaxis? Periodontal maintenance procedures include a predominance of power scaling with thin inserts to access and debride the depths of periodontal pockets. Your patient may need anesthesia of some type. The goal is thorough debridement of pathogens that have repopulated in the sulcus. Periodontal pathogens reside on and in calculus, on root surface biofilm with no calculus, in sulcular epithelium, and free-floating in the sulcus. Most likely, a six-point periodontal probing is necessary in order to re-assess changes that have occurred in pocket depths. Irrigation post-procedure with an appropriate antimicrobial such as Povidone iodine or chlorhexidine might be needed. You may need to apply desensitizing agents, such as Colgate's Pro-Relief™ with a rubber cup, if your patient has sensitive exposed root surfaces. If your patient has exposed root surfaces, which is often the case with periodontal patients, any polishing should be with low-abrasion pastes.

How to Explain the Differences to Patients

If a patient is not completely healthy and needs continued periodontal maintenance, one way to explain the difference is to say: "The reason your fee is higher is because your gums still aren't completely healthy. If they were healthy, my job would be a lot easier and the fees would be the same." "It all depends on you. If you do all the things we advise you to do at home, every day, there's a good chance your gums will heal. When they're healthy, you won't need anything more complex than an ordinary preventive prophy."

Some patients will need more convincing. In their minds the problem isn't their gums, it's your fee. They think the practice is taking advantage of them. It's an emotional issue. The problem isn't that they don't understand what you're trying to say; it's that they don't believe it. The patient thinks that the practice is trying to cheat him because he's being charged more for the same procedure than his spouse was charged. Trying to explain the factual differences between a D4910 and a D1110 is the wrong approach with these patients, because they're not thinking intellectually. It's an emotional response to a perception of unfairness. The patient is mad because, from his point of view, you're charging him more money for the same amount of time. Since you're the one who's charging him, you're part of the problem and your explanations are suspect.

These patients are going to need compelling evidence, something besides your (from their perspective) self-serving explanation. What's needed is an independent authority, something other than your words that the patient can believe in. So, what kinds of authoritative, compelling evidence can you provide that the practice isn't trying to bilk him, other than your say-so? One way is to show the patient photographic proof. If you have intraoral photographs of both your patient and his spouse, the photos will help the patient see the same differences you see. The clinical differences, like inflamed tissue and bleeding, are obvious, even to a layman. Note: HIPAA regulations prevent a hygienist from discussing specifics of a spouse's periodontal condition with the other spouse unless given written permission. It is permissible to provide information about the transmissibility of periodontal pathogens between individuals.

Charts are another type of independent authority, but they'll need to be graphic so the differences are clear for anyone to see. A device like the Florida Probe™, for instance, can transform dull probe data into striking, colorful charts. Some computerized patient-management software programs and stand-alone devices and programs like the Dental R.A.T.® and PerioPal® also produce impressive probing charts. Even giving the patient a hand mirror and showing him how his gums are bleeding and his spouse's gums are not bleeding would be a powerful emotional tool. The main point is this: The independent authority has to be highly visual and vivid to counter the emotional belief that they're being cheated.

Another approach is to use an actual independent authority. Physicians do this all the time by getting lab tests, and an increasing number of dentists are starting to use lab tests as well. There are four outside labs that have periodontal tests. Two are culturing services: Oral Microbiology Testing Service (OMTS), and Oral Microbiology Testing Lab (OMTL). The other two are DNA tests: OralDNA Labs®, and micro-IDent®plus. All four tests can detect pathogens that are highly associated with periodontal diseases. There is also a third-party statistical test, PreViser™, based on clinical findings that estimates the likelihood of periodontal disease. In addition to these outside tests, there are two microbiological tests that can be used chairside. BANA™ is an enzymatic test for periodontal pathogens, and BioScan™ is a video microscopy test. Any of these tests would provide patients with the kind of authoritative proof they need in order to believe that they have a gum condition that requires a different type of treatment than their spouse.

Resolving the Problem

Your job as a dental hygienist is twofold. You have to determine which type of periodic care is needed, patient by patient, and you have to convince patients that they need that care and are getting their money's worth. Once you understand the differences and realize why the patient is upset, you'll become a better therapist, and there won't be nearly so many "failures to communicate."

http://www.floridaprobe.com/

http://www.dentalrat.com/

http://www.temple.edu/dentistry/perio/omts.html

http://www.usc.edu/hsc/dental/OMTL/OMTL_P01.html

http://www.oraldna.com/ http://www.hain-diagnostics.com/

http://www.previser.com/ https://www.oratec.net/

"Documentation Dilemma"

Dear Dianne,

I am a hygienist who works two days per week at the front desk and two days in clinical hygiene. The office where I work has three dentists and five assistants. The problem is that they are AWFUL with documentation. Their chart notes are scanty and often incomplete. Today when I reviewed the charts, there was one new patient chart with a blank medical history and one for a patient who had not been in for the past three years with no health questions answered. Both patients received antibiotics and pain medications. Over and over, I beg the assistants and doctors to update the medical history and be more concise with chart notes. Do you have any helpful hints to help me make my point with the doctors and assistants in our office to improve their documentation?

Trying to Avoid a Lawsuit

Dear Trying,

The dental chart is a legal document. It is the first line of defense in a malpractice suit. When a patient decides to file a lawsuit against a dentist, the dental chart becomes the single most important piece of information relative to the suit. A poorly written, inadequate narrative can be the most damaging evidence against a clinician.

The ADA questioned several of the major malpractice insurance carriers about various record-keeping errors that they had observed in malpractice proceedings. The number one record-keeping error they identified was failure to have a treatment plan. The number two record-keeping error was failure to update the medical history. The medical history should be updated at **every** patient visit by the clinician. At least once per year, the patient should be asked to verify that his/her current medical history is correct by signing the form (or tablet in paperless offices). Most risk management experts recommend having the patient fill out a completely new history about every three years.

There have been numerous malpractice cases where patients were prescribed drugs by dental professionals that were clearly contraindicated by the patient's medical history. This brand of inattentiveness can lead to serious consequences for patient and clinician.

You might be interested to know that one of the top reasons clinicians lose malpractice cases is because when the clinician finds out s/he is being sued for malpractice, somebody alters the chart. Why do clinicians alter the chart? The main reason is because the clinician failed to record thorough chart notes at the time of treatment, and the clinician is trying to make it appear thorough *after the fact.*

Recently, I spoke with an attorney who shared with me that he lost the biggest case of his entire career because the doctor altered the chart after he found out he was being sued. The doctor tried to insert additional comments and make them appear contemporaneous to the original entry. An expert with the court determined that two different pens had been used and was able to state that the original entry had been altered. Of course, this revelation destroyed the doctor's credibility and ultimately caused him to lose the case.

When people write incomplete chart notes, the usual excuse is lack of time. It becomes a habit to whiz through the day without being concerned with recording details of patient visits in the practice. More often, the problem is not lack of time but rather lack of due diligence. People get sloppy with record-keeping. The fact is that in a court of law or before a state dental board, incomplete records could prove to be the most damaging factor to the clinician. Remember that in the eyes of the law or a state dental board, if something is not recorded in the chart, it never happened. Clinicians have a legal and ethical responsibility to record complete and accurate information. Dental professionals are without excuse for poor, inadequate records.

Thorough documentation includes the complete and accurate recording of all collected data, treatment planned and provided, recommendations, and other information relevant to patient care and treatment. All entries should record information objectively and comply with HIPAA regulations.

Some charting tips include:

NEVER alter or add to original chart notes. If you need to amend an entry, make a new entry as an addendum to the original entry.

For paper charts, do not skip lines between entries. Do not leave white space. Do not write in margins or below the last line, and always use permanent ink.

Handwritten notes **must be legible.**

Record events of the visit in the order they happen. Record all materials used, especially anesthetics (kind and how much).

Be consistent with abbreviations. Some risk management experts advise against using the abbreviation 'WNL' because it is ambiguous.

Stick to the facts, and do not use unclear verbiage, such as "Patient seemed angry." Rather, "Patient said, 'I'm sick and tired of this sore tooth.' "

Do not ever record disparaging entries in a chart that you would not want a jury to see, such as "PITA patient."

According to Marsha Freeman (www.marshafreeman.com), chart entries should include the following:

Date_____

1. Reason for the visit

2. Thorough review of health and dental history

3. Patient's chief complaint in his/her own words

4. Symptoms (symptomatic or asymptomatic)

5. Clinician's visual findings

6. Diagnostic records

7. Doctor's examination

8. Doctor's diagnosis

9. Doctor's recommended treatment

10. Discussion with patient and his/her choice of treatment

11. Treatment rendered

12. Items given to patient

Next visit_____ Signature _____

You need to sound the warning trumpet to everyone in the practice regarding the possible consequences of inadequate record-keeping, which includes updating medical histories. Those consequences include loss of a malpractice suit, suspension or revocation of license, even jail time. I suggest you conduct a staff meeting and go over the record-keeping protocol from a defensive standpoint. Let everyone know you have the best interests of patients and clinicians at the forefront of the discussion. Unfortunately, it may take a lawsuit or board complaint to arouse some people from their sloppy record-keeping slumber. For sure, that would be an unpleasant wake-up call!

Best wishes,

Dianne

"Medical History Update Dilemma"

Dear Dianne,

I know it is important to update medical histories on our patients. What concerns me are those patients who hardly even look at the form and simply sign their names. Also, filling out a new medical history seems to be a source of frustration for some patients. Some will scowl or reluctantly take the clipboard with a big sigh. Are there clear guidelines on how often to ask patients to complete a new medical history? I have heard several different recommendations. The protocol in our practice is to have the patient fill out a completely new form once per year. We ask them to fill out a shortened form every six months. Is this correct, or is it too much?

Thanks,

Cathy J.

Dear Cathy,

Your inquiry provoked a memory of a man I observed in a dental office. When the business assistant handed him a clipboard with a medical history and asked him for an update, he angrily jerked the clipboard from her and drew a diagonal line through the center. On the line he wrote in large letters, "NO CHANGES" and slammed it back down on the counter. The assistant and I were shocked at this man's apparent rudeness. His behavior showed his obvious displeasure at being asked to fill out a medical history form.

Why did he react this way to her simple request? I do not think it was because he enjoyed being rude. Rather, he saw the request as an imposition. He resented having to outline to this office the same information again and again. A weak analogy can be drawn by considering how you would feel if someone asked you the same question every time they saw you. Attendant to this is the hurried pace of so many people in their daily lives. They do not like to waste time, and to them, filling out our forms is a waste of time.

Also, consider the growing problem of adult illiteracy in the United States. The results of the National Adult Literacy Survey in 2002 (conducted by the U.S. Department of Education) said that almost half of the U.S. population is either functionally illiterate or only marginally literate.

According to the American Medical Association's publication, *Health Literacy, a Manual for Clinicians,* several studies have revealed that those with limited literacy skills do not understand or are not aware of concepts basic to common diseases. Therefore, it is entirely possible that many of our patients are intimidated by our forms that contain words they do not understand and cannot read.

Please understand it is not your patient's responsibility to provide you with a complete medical history. Rather, it is YOUR responsibility to obtain a complete medical history from your patient. This is why many medical practices have instituted a strategy of having a nurse sit down with the patient and go through the history with the nurse writing the documentation. The patient merely signs at the completion of the interview.

The ADA recently obtained information from several of the major malpractice insurance carriers regarding record-keeping errors that played a part in various malpractice proceedings. The number one error noted was "no treatment plan," and number two was "health history is not clearly documented or not updated regularly." This highlights a shortcoming in many dental practices.

I queried the ADA Council on Scientific Affairs with this question: How often should a patient be required to fill out a completely new medical history? The answer I received was that there is not a clear guideline, but medical histories should be updated at *every patient visit.* This does not mean you have the patient fill out a new form at each visit, but it does mean that the clinician inquires at each visit about possible changes in the medical status of the patient. Further, the clinician should document that the medical history was updated.

The frequency with which you ask patients to fill out a completely new form should depend on the patient. Common sense dictates that patients who have complicated medical histories need complete updating more often than the average healthy adult patient. A three-year rule for new forms is not unreasonable. My advice is for you to sit with the patient and personally update the medical history form by asking the questions and recording the patient's answers for any patients with medical complications. Patients should be asked to bring a list of their medications to be included as well. Also, personally update for any patient who displays even the slightest consternation at completing your forms.

Your practice of having patients fill out a new form once per year is not wrong, although the 'paper blizzard' you are creating is not necessary. My feeling is that anything we do that causes our patients unnecessary frustration does not promote good patient relationships and therefore should be modified.

There will be occasions where information provided by the patient about medical conditions will necessitate a telephone call to the patient's physician. Please make sure any consultations with a physician are recorded in the patient record.

According to Burton Pollack, DDS, MPH, JD, author of *Law and Risk Management in Dental Practice* (2002), there should be a few open-ended questions on the health history. "Health history forms on which the patient can only make check marks, circles, or underlines indicating yes or no answers can raise doubts as to who entered the responses if the health history is reviewed in a judicial proceeding. Your history forms should be designed so that patients write their responses to open-ended questions."

In consultation with various attorneys, it is my understanding that signatures never expire. Please have your patients sign any new forms they complete. However, updates to those forms do not require their signature again. Of course, the clinician should sign the update entries in the interim.

Patients have various reasons for balking at our forms. Whatever the reason, we can make this a non-issue by assisting our patients through the maze of questions and medical terms. We take pressure off our patients by showing a personal interest in their medical health with our upfront attention to this very important part of comprehensive patient care. It is part of 'walking the walk and talking the talk' that oral health is connected to overall physical health.

Best wishes,

Dianne

"Blood Pressures and Standard of Care"

Dear Dianne,

After attending your lecture in Portsmouth, N.H., I suggested to the doctor with whom I work that we should start taking blood pressures on our patients. The doctor was amenable to the idea, although he felt we probably would not find many people with undiagnosed hypertension. Wow, were we ever surprised! In the first four months after implementing blood pressure screening, we identified 10 patients with hypertension that we referred to their physician. Several of these patients have returned to thank us for identifying a silent condition with serious consequences if left untreated. Thanks for addressing this topic and helping me become a better hygienist.

Sincerely,

Pam MacDonald, RDH, BS

Dear Pam,

Congratulations on your decision to ramp up your patient care! By performing blood pressure screenings, you are walking the walk and talking the talk that preventive care specialists (hygienists) are interested in the patient as a total being, and that the mouth is connected to the rest of the body.

We know that cardiovascular disease is the number one killer of Americans today, both men and women. According to the American Heart Association, there has been an alarming increase in the number of children with hypertension and high cholesterol, most likely from consuming a high-fat, high-cholesterol diet, and getting inadequate exercise.

For review, blood pressure is the pressure that blood exerts against the walls of the arteries. The amount of pressure depends upon the strength and rate of the heart's contraction, the volume of blood in the circulatory system, and the elasticity of the arteries.

When air is pumped into the blood pressure cuff, the inflated cuff presses down on the arteries. This stops the flow of blood, and no sound can be heard through the stethoscope. As the air is slowly released from the cuff, the pressure of the cuff becomes less than the blood pressure and the blood flow returns. The pressure at which the flow resumes is called the systolic pressure. It represents the blood pressure when the heart is contracting. As more air is let out of the cuff, the sounds become muffled. The pressure at this point is called the diastolic pressure. It represents the blood pressure while the heart is relaxing. Therefore, the first number is the systolic pressure and is normally around 120 millimeters. The second number, the diastolic pressure, is normally around 80.

Hypertension is the most important etiologic factor for cardiovascular disease in the USA. Also, cardiovascular and atherosclerotic complications are the major cause of morbidity and mortality in patients with primary hypertension. In adults, systolic blood pressure elevations are usually considered to be more a determinant of cardiovascular risk than are diastolic blood pressure elevations. Hypertension accelerates the development and progression of atherosclerosis.

Hypertension is defined as a persistent elevation in blood pressure that is considered to be higher than normal. More specifically, the Joint National Committee on Detection, Evaluation, and Treatment of High Blood Pressure defines hypertension as a systolic blood pressure greater than or equal to 140 mm Hg or a diastolic blood pressure greater than or equal to 90 mm Hg as recorded during two or more readings on two or more occasions (office visits).

Blood Pressure Guidelines

Pressure	Normal	Pre-Hypertensive	Stage 1 Hypertension	Stage 2 Hypertension
Systolic	< 120	120–139	140–159	More than 160
Diastolic	< 80	80–89	90–99	More than 100
Treatment				
Otherwise Healthy	None	None	Diuretics for most, possibly other medications	Two-drug combo, one is usually a diuretic
With other diseases*	None	Medically treat diseases	Multiple medications	Multiple medications

- *Previous heart attack, diabetes, kidney disease or certain other diseases

- Systolic pressure is measured when the vessel wall contracts

- Diastolic pressure is measured when the vessel wall relaxes between beats

- In people over 50, systolic pressure is more important than diastolic pressure

(Guidelines based on **The Seventh Report of the Joint National Committee on Prevention, Detection, Evaluation, and Treatment of High Blood Pressure, 2003** *(http://hyper.ahajournals.org/cgi/content/full/42/6/1206),* Glick M, The new blood pressure guidelines, J Am Dent Assn, 135:585-86, May 2004, and* **Medical Emergencies in the Dental Office,** *Stanley F. Malamed, DDS, Fifth Edition, 1999.)*

In people aged up to 50, both diastolic blood pressure and systolic blood pressure are independently associated with cardiovascular risk. At age 50, systolic blood pressure is far more important than the level of diastolic blood pressure in predicting the risk of coronary heart disease, left ventricular hypertrophy, congestive heart failure, renal failure, and mortality in people with hypertension. At age 60 years, however, as vascular compliance is reduced, an increasing systolic blood pressure and a lower diastolic blood pressure increase cardiovascular risk.

Age-related physiological changes explain the frequent development of isolated systolic hypertension in older people. Younger people have a highly distensible aorta, which expands during systole and minimizes any subsequent rise in blood pressure. Most older people, however, develop progressive stiffening of their arterial tree as they age, which leads to a continuous elevation in systolic blood pressure (*British Medical Journal* 2002;325:917-918.)

The 'safe' range for treating patients varies. Some people continue to exhibit high blood pressure readings, even with medications. So, "high" is their normal. Most medical/dental professionals agree that 160/100 is the danger zone. Anesthetics containing epinephrine would be contraindicated for such patients. The best course of action is to interface with the patient's physician when high blood pressure is detected. A simple phone call to compare what the patient's last recorded blood pressure was in their office might indicate a change in blood pressure.

Did you know that some states have written blood pressure screening or monitoring into their written standards of care? For example, this excerpt comes from the Texas "Dental Practice—Standard of Care" document concerning blood pressure monitoring:

*SBDE Rule 108.7(2)(B) states that the initial limited physical examination should include, but shall not necessarily be limited to, blood pressure, and pulse/heart rate as may be indicated for each patient. The SBDE has determined that the minimum standard of care requires the recording of **at least an initial baseline blood pressure/pulse reading during the initial limited physical examination of a dental patient.** The dental practitioner should also record blood pressure and pulse heart rate as indicated for invasive procedures and as required by Board rules regarding procedures involving sedation and anesthesia.*

Epidemiology

It is estimated that at least 68 million Americans have hypertension, or one in three Americans. It is also estimated about 30% of the American population takes some kind of hypertension medication. Primary (or essential) hypertension has no clearly identifiable etiology, and accounts for 90–95% of cases. An estimated 10–15% of white adults and 20–30% of black adults in the USA currently have primary hypertension. Between 70–90% of affected individuals have mild (stage 1 or early stage 2) primary hypertension. The age of onset of primary hypertension usually ranges between ages 25 and 55. There is no clearly defined sex predominance for the disease.

Etiology and Pathogenesis

Hypertension is classified by etiology as being either primary (essential, idiopathic) or secondary. Current evidence suggests the disease is caused by varying combinations of many potential interacting factors. Patients with primary hypertension do not appear to share any one, or a specific combination of, suspected etiologic factors.

No clearly established genetic pattern has been established for primary hypertension. However, blood pressure levels appear to have strong familial tendencies. Children with one (and to a greater degree, two) hypertensive parent(s) tend to have higher blood pressures and are perceived to be at an increased risk to develop hypertension.

Complications of untreated hypertension are numerous. The degree of damage to susceptible "target" organs is closely related to both the duration and severity of the hypertension. These complications include:

■ Cardiovascular disease: Hypertension is the most important etiologic factor for cardiovascular disease in the USA. Also, cardiovascular and atherosclerotic complications are the major cause of morbidity and mortality in patients with primary hypertension. In adults, systolic blood pressure elevations are usually considered to be more a determinant of cardiovascular risk than are diastolic blood pressure elevations. Hypertension accelerates the development and progression of atherosclerosis (leading to peripheral and coronary vascular insufficiency), and subsequently increases the patient's risk for myocardial infarction. Hypertension also causes left ventricular hypertrophy, which may result in congestive heart failure, ventricular arrhythmias, myocardial ischemia, and sudden death. Hypertension is a major etiology for both dissecting and atherosclerotic aortic aneurysms, and also acts as an exacerbating factor in the progression of these conditions. Retinal vascular narrowing, hemorrhages, exudates, and papilledema are also consequences of hypertension.

■ Cerebrovascular disease: Hypertension increases the risk of cerebral vascular insufficiency, and is a also major cause of stroke (cerebrovascular accident), especially those resulting from intercerebral hemorrhage, cerebral infarction, or subarachnoid hemorrhage.

■ Renal disease: Untreated hypertension may lead to nephrosclerosis and accounts for 40% of cases of chronic renal failure (end-stage renal disease). Hypertension may also accelerate the progression of other forms of renal disease such as diabetic nephropathy.

Physical and Dental Exam

Establish the patient's baseline blood pressure at the first dental appointment. Two to three blood pressure measurements separated by at least five minutes should be taken, and the results averaged to determine the patient's baseline blood pressure. The patient's baseline blood pressure will serve as a point of reference from which to make decisions for the emergency management of the patient should a cardiovascular or adverse reaction develop during dental treatment. The patient's blood

The Consummate Dental Hygienist

pressure should be checked at all subsequent appointments prior to the use of a local anesthesia.

Dental Management Precautions

- Reduce stress and anxiety during dental treatment: Consider the use of N_2O-O_2 inhalation sedation and/or premedication with oral anti-anxiety medications such as benzodiazepines.

- Do not use local anesthetics with vasoconstrictors in patients with uncontrolled or poorly controlled hypertension. This is defined as any patient with a systolic blood pressure greater than or equal to 180 mmHg and/or a diastolic blood pressure greater than or equal to 100 mmHg.

- For patients with controlled hypertension, where the use of local anesthetics with vasoconstrictors is not contraindicated because of potential drug interactions, limit the total dose of vasoconstrictor to maximum of 0.04 mg of epinephrine (2.2 carpules of 2% lidocaine with 1:100,000 epinephrine) or 0.2 mg of levonordefrin (2.2 carpules of 2% carbocaine with 1:20,000 levonordefrin).

Treatment Planning Considerations

There are no specific treatment planning modifications or consider-ations for patients with controlled hypertension. However, no elective dental procedures should be performed on a patient with severe or uncontrolled hypertension. Additionally, the clinician should avoid stimulating the gag reflex in patients with a history of hypertension. Uncontrolled hypertension can also cause excessive bleeding during dental procedures. The clinician should take into account that some patients may be unable to lie back comfortably for treatment due to pulmonary congestion.

In Conclusion

Untreated hypertension generally has no symptoms—hence it is the "silent killer." Every dental hygienist is professionally educated while in hygiene school in taking blood pressures on patients. Blood pressure recordings are taken routinely on every patient seen by the dental or dental hygiene student. It is the standard of care. Why is it that so many clinicians neglect this valuable service to patients upon finishing school and entering the real world of clinical practice?

Although we can offer many excuses as to why we do not take blood pressures on our patients, every obstacle can be met and overcome with planning. Given the dire consequences of untreated or undiagnosed hypertension, e.g., heart failure, strokes, and kidney failure, helping our patients identify hypertension is a valuable service that may just save lives! If you are not routinely taking blood pressures, start immediately. Doing less is operating below the standard of care.

David and Dianne Watterson, the author, and Lynne Slim, RDH, MS, at Under One Roof, Chicago, Illinois.

"Prescribing Antibiotics"

Dear Dianne,

The doctor I work with uses the former premedication guidelines which require a post-treatment dosage, typically six hours after treatment. A recent example was a patient who had a total knee replacement last year. The premedication given was erythromycin 500 mg with the dosage of two tablets one hour before dental treatment and then one tablet six hours later. I actually had a copy of the most current guidelines and showed the doctor, but he seemed unconcerned and did not comment. I know he is aware of the new guidelines.

Another premedication dilemma is when a physician mandates a premedication protocol that is outside the guidelines. An example is a physician in our city who recommends antibiotic premedication for dental procedures after breast implant surgery for one year following placement of implants. Does he have any basis for this protocol? A cardiologist in our city follows the former guidelines requiring a post-treatment dosage. What's with that?

I feel stuck in the middle. I'm just an employee, so I'm not calling the shots. But I'm smart enough to know that we are supposed to follow the current guidelines regarding premedication. How should I respond, and is there any liability risk?

Concerned Hygienist

Dear Concerned,

It is true that current premedication guidelines for the prevention of infections in artificial joints do not require any post-treatment dosages of antibiotics. This information is taken directly from the AAOS document regarding suitable premedication options: (Premedication Guidelines for Joint/Orthopedic Patients, Feb. 2009 http://www.aaos.org/)

Suggested antibiotic prophylaxis regimens*

- ◼ Patients not allergic to penicillin: cephalexin, cephradine or amoxicillin: 2 grams orally one hour prior to dental procedure.

- Patients not allergic to penicillin and unable to take oral medications: cefazolin 1 gram or ampicillin 2 grams IM/IV one hour prior to the procedure.

- Patients allergic to penicillin: clindamycin: 600 mg orally one hour prior to the dental procedure.

- Patients allergic to penicillin and unable to take oral medications: clindamycin 600 mg IV, one hour prior to the procedure.

No second doses are recommended for any of these dosing regimens.

Interestingly, the AAOS revised its guidelines in February 2009 to state that any patient with a full replacement should have **lifetime** premedication coverage before dental procedures. The former guidelines mandated premedication antibiotics for a two-year period following placement. (You can read the full document at: http://www.aaos.org/about/papers/advistmt/1033.asp) At a time when most epidemiologists feel we should be curtailing the use of antibiotics because of resistant strains of disease-causing organisms, the actions of the AAOS are surprising. Two years ago, the AHA modified its guidelines for people with various heart conditions and discontinued premedication antibiotics for several conditions that were previously indicated. The actions of the AHA were in response to the increasing emergence of drug-resistant pathogens, such as MRSA and Clostridium difficile.

If a doctor chooses to follow an antibiotic regimen that is different from the guidelines, s/he is not adhering to the current standards of care (which are stipulated in the guidelines). The danger is if the patient has an untoward reaction, the doctor who did the prescribing will be liable. The liability risk is greater if the doctor does not follow the most current guidelines. The other danger is resistance issues. No one should be prescribing antibiotics above what is necessary for a minimum effective dosage. The post-treatment dose is not warranted or recommended.

It seems that some physicians make up their own guidelines or follow previous guidelines. In cases where the patient has been advised contrary to the established guidelines, it is in the dentist's best interest to require the **physician** to do the prescribing. If a dentist agrees to become a party to practices outside the standard of care, that dentist risks liability through complicity.

It is my contention (and many others who study liability issues in dentistry) that dentists should get out of the premedication business—period. If a patient has a physical condition that warrants premedication, let the physician who diagnosed the condition be responsible for pre-medication antibiotics and any associated risks. If a dentist prescribes a premedication antibiotic for a patient and that patient has an untoward reaction or succumbs to anaphylaxis, the prescribing dentist is liable. Dentists should stick to prescribing antibiotics for dental conditions, such as infections, abscesses, etc. This lessens the possibility of liability related to untoward reactions.

Unfortunately, there can be exceptions to most rules. Such is the case in patients who are severely immunocompromised. In a recent court case, a dentist opted to extract an abscessed tooth from a woman with poorly controlled diabetes without giving her a pre-extraction antibiotic. The patient developed a serious infection and died after spending 20 months on life support. Her spouse sued the dentist and won a $2.6 million jury verdict (which is under appeal). According to the report, the key issue was whether the patient should have been given an antibiotic prior to the extraction. An ADA recommendation states that dentists "consider systemic antibiotics for uncontrolled diabetic patients who have frequent infections or heal poorly." Numerous studies have found that infection is a risk for diabetic patients and can make it more difficult to control blood glucose levels. A 2000 study published in the *Journal of the American Dental Association* concluded that, because insulin-dependent diabetics are particularly susceptible to infections, "antibiotic coverage for invasive dental procedures is recommended in patients with poorly controlled or uncontrolled diabetes." (*JADA*, March 2000, Vol. 131:3, pp. 366-374).

As a hygienist, it is your duty to document the facts. You are not liable for the actions of another person, such as if the doctor chooses to practice outside the standards of care. While any departure from the established guidelines is risky, it is your job to document what was prescribed and advisement of current guidelines. If a physician uses a non-standard protocol, have that physician fax a copy of the premedication prescription to keep in your patient's chart.

Best wishes,

Dianne

"Fluoride Varnish Conundrum"

Dear Dianne,

Recently, my boss went to a continuing education meeting where he learned about expanded use of fluoride varnish. He made the decision to mandate application of fluoride varnish on all our adult patients. The reasons given were that varnish is very good at helping control caries and sensitivity, and that all patients benefit from it. Of course, there's the extra $40 added to the patient fee as well.

What we are finding out is that dental benefits do not cover adult fluoride treatments, and many of our patients have become irate over this issue. One patient said she felt it was "overtreatment." Some patients have complained about the unpleasant feeling of the varnish on their teeth. I know the doctor wants us to push this, but I feel very uncomfortable with the whole premise. It feels like a way to gouge people—a money thing. Yet, I also know fluoride varnish is a very good product. Can you help me see how I should approach this problem clearly?

Needing Clarity

Dear Needing,

Several issues have surfaced in your post. First off, it sounds like the doctor heard about using fluoride varnish treatments as a 'profit center' in the practice. Touting any treatment as a 'profit center' reeks of questionable motivations and leads to unnecessary treatment. Yet the math is impressive. Consider eight adult patients each day at $40/fluoride each. That's an additional $320 each day. Multiply that by four days and you get $1,280 per week. Multiply that times 48 weeks, and you get a whopping $61,440 additional revenue per year! Even if only half our adult patients get fluoride, that's $30,700—a significant amount. So it is easy to see why some doctors are quick to proclaim the benefits of fluoride varnish. The question is, who does it really benefit?

Does every adult patient need a fluoride treatment? To answer this question, we need a credible source. In May 2006, an article appeared in the *Journal of the American Dental Association* titled "Professionally Applied Topical Fluoride—Executive Summary of Evidence-Based Clinical Recommendations." The article was compiled by the ADA Council on Scientific Affairs. This well-written and comprehensive information source recommends that we base our decisions on fluoride administration on the patient's risk category. In the panel conclusions, it is stated: "Patients whose caries risk is low, as defined in this document, may not receive additional benefit from professional topical fluoride application." Low risk is defined for all age groups as "No incipient or cavitated primary or secondary carious lesions during the last three years and no factors that may increase caries risk."

Factors that increase caries risk include but are not limited to:

- poor oral hygiene
- developmental or acquired enamel defects
- eating disorders
- drug or alcohol abuse
- active orthodontic treatment
- xerostomia

The document further states that "two or more applications of fluoride varnish per year are effective in preventing caries in high-risk populations." Read the whole document for more information on risk factors and levels at http://ebd.ada.org/ClinicalRecommendations.aspx.

Let's suppose that I am your patient. I have excellent oral hygiene; I have not had any caries for over 20 years; I eat a healthful diet and avoid sugary drinks; I have no sensitivity issues; I do not have any medical problems that cause xerostomia or any of the other risk factors. Do I need fluoride varnish? Absolutely not. In fact, the recommendations state there would be no additional benefit for someone like me. Fluoride varnish is not recommended for me based on my lack of risk factors.

How about Joe Blow, a 40-something patient with terrible oral hygiene and high caries index? Would he benefit from fluoride varnish? Most likely, yes.

Our education teaches us to make clinical decisions based on need. Just as you would not recommend orthodontics to a patient with straight teeth, no TMJ issues, and perfect bite, you should not recommend fluoride varnish to patients without certain risk factors. Blanket mandates on treatment are seldom appropriate for every patient.

Another issue is the unpleasant feeling of fluoride varnish on the teeth. When the average person comes in for her professional 'cleaning' visit, she enjoys that nice slick feeling after having the teeth polished. However, fluoride varnish leaves a waxy residue that is difficult to remove. It is most unpleasant to have fluoride varnish gunked all over the teeth. I'd wager that most dentists who push fluoride varnish on their patients have never had it applied to their own teeth. If they experienced it, they might feel a little sympathy for their patients.

A third issue is benefits coverage. I do not know of any benefits carrier that covers adult fluoride varnish. So patients who are very insurance-dependent will be upset when they find out they have to pay out of pocket for something extra that was unpleasant and unwanted. Please remember this: To unpleasantly surprise a patient is to lose a patient.

Third-party benefits become a side issue for people with multiple risk factors for caries. The evidence is clear that such patients benefit from topical application of fluoride, either fluoride varnish or a four-minute fluoride gel treatment. Those patients should have the benefits spelled out, and then be allowed to be part of the decision-making process.

A sure way to harm—or even destroy—a dental practice is for patients to develop a perception of being ripped off. Patients are not stupid! When patients have an unpleasant experience in the office, they will tell 20 or more people. When we base treatment decisions on profit motive, we eventually lose the patient's trust. If we lose their trust, we lose them AND anyone they might have referred to us in the future.

After the death of my husband, I had to attend to my own car maintenance, which was something totally foreign to me. Once when I took my car for an oil change, the mechanic told me I needed a very expensive brake job. He expounded on the dangers to my car and me if I procrastinated. For some reason, I doubted his word. On my brother's advice, I took my car to a different garage for a second opinion. The mechanic removed my tires and inspected my brakes thoroughly. He could not find any reason to do a brake job on my car. Needless to say, the first garage will never get any more of my business.

We should treat people like we would want to be treated if we were in their position, i.e., fairly and ethically. To do otherwise is immoral, unethical, and just plain wrong.

My point is that *all* adult patients do not need fluoride treatments, but those with certain risk factors may benefit from topical fluoride. Fluoride varnish is a fabulous product that should be used where indicated. As with all clinical treatment, we should base the decision to use adjuncts on the patient's need according to their risk factors and not on blanket mandates that may be inappropriate.

Best wishes,

Dianne

"The Smoker"

Dear Dianne,

Recently I had a female patient, 40 years of age, who had not had any dental care for four years. Her health history was unremarkable. She smokes one pack a day of cigarettes. Since she had not been in for quite awhile, the doctor saw her first for an exam. He classified her periodontal condition as a Type II needing four quadrants of root planing/scaling, and she was scheduled with me.

At the appointment, I saw that the tissue overall looked tight with some redness in the papillae. There was no apparent bone loss on the radiographs. Probing depths on the right side were only 2-3 mm with one 4 mm on the distobuccal of #3 with generalized moderate bleeding. There was no recession or mobility.

Upon scaling, I found light supragingival calculus on the lingual lower anterior with generalized moderate/heavy subgingival calculus, lightly tenacious, with moderate bleeding. I was able to complete her right side in the one-hour appointment.

After the patient left, I let my doctor know that I was uncomfortable calling this patient an SRP patient and that she should have been a multiple adult prophy patient. He went over the definitions from the CDT for prophy and SRP:

> *Adult prophy D1110: Removal of plaque, calculus and stains from the tooth structures in the permanent and transitional dentition. It is intended to control local irritational factors.*

> *Periodontal scaling and root planing four or more teeth per quadrant D4341: This procedure involves instrumentation of the crown and root surfaces of the teeth to remove plaque and calculus from these surfaces. It is indicated for patients with periodontal disease and is therapeutic, not prophylactic, in nature. Root planing is the definitive procedure designed for the removal of cementum and dentin that is rough, and/or permeated by calculus or contaminated with toxins or microorganisms. Some soft-tissue removal occurs. This procedure MAY be used as a definitive treatment in some stages of periodontal disease and/or as part of a pre-surgical procedures in others.*

The doctor determined that this patient needed SRP because she is a periodontal case Type II and needed therapeutic care. If I understood correctly, the doctor felt this patient needed SRP because of the difficulty of the calculus and the amount of time to treat her. My understanding of adult prophy is there is no attachment loss. I would have typed her as a Class I with no apparent bone loss needing multiple prophys. What is the appropriate classification for this patient? Who is right, the doctor or me?

Confused Over Classification

Dear Confused,

I agree with the doctor on the Type II classification for this patient, but I do not agree that the patient needed four one-hour appointments to treat. Let's consider the facts.

Fact 1—This patient is a smoker. Smoking and diabetes are the top two risk factors for periodontal disease; therefore this particular patient's risk is greatly increased.

Fact 2—Smoking masks periodontal disease. Smokers often have firm, pale pink gingiva that doesn't bleed easily. In fact, the tissue can be downright leather-like (fibrotic). Being from North Carolina where tobacco is widely grown, I treated lots of smokers. I will even admit to being fooled a couple of times into thinking a particular patient's tissue was fine since it didn't bleed and was very firm, until I inserted a periodontal probe—especially at the mid-lingual areas of maxillary molars—and discovered deep pockets. Facial and lingual bone loss may not be seen on radiographs.

Fact 3—The amount of bleeding observed (moderate) with this patient indicates therapeutic care is needed. A prophylaxis is intended to control irritation, whereas your patient already had significant irritation as evidenced by bleeding. Therefore, a therapeutic approach is warranted.

Dental hygiene clinical education focuses heavily on calculus removal techniques. Hygienists can become so calculus-focused that they forget they are fighting a microbial battle. In fact, the former endpoint of "glassy smooth root surfaces" has been replaced by debridement with minimal damage to intact cementum. Don't misunderstand—you need to remove as much calculus as possible. But calculus is not the cause of periodontal problems. Microbes that live in and on the calculus and sulcus area are the real culprits in the initiation and progression of periodontal diseases.

Periodontal diseases are chronic and begin in shallow sulci. Early in the disease process, the patient may not exhibit significant bone loss. In fact, bone loss is a historical marker of the destruction that has already taken place. If you can avert bone destruction by engaging a therapeutic approach early in the process, your patient will benefit greatly.

However, the patient's smoking habit will greatly increase her risk of future serious periodontal problems. If she is unwilling to quit, then you must treat her with increased awareness and diligence and not allow fibrotic tissue to fool you. After all, if the tissue looks firm and pink—as if often the case with smokers—periodontal disease is probably lurking in the shadows.

The treatment protocol for early periodontitis patients involves a combination of prophylaxis and site-specific periodontal scaling. Following is a description and recommended treatment protocol.

Type II—Early Periodontitis

Slight bone loss is detected with some pockets in the 4-6 mm range. Some areas may need anesthesia to scale thoroughly. However, the disease has not progressed to the point of furcation involvement or mobility. Also, recession must be charted, not only because it shows previous disease, but because it is a more accurate representation of the patient's periodontal status. Many insurance companies do not pay benefits for root planing unless there is at least 4 mm of attachment loss (not just probing depth). Attachment loss is the addition of the pocket measurement plus recession. The early periodontitis patient will have three or fewer teeth in the quadrant that are periodontally involved. They will require site-specific periodontal treatment. The remainder of the dentition is appropriately treated with a prophylaxis—D1110.

1st visit–prophylaxis for non-periodontally involved teeth   Code 1110

2nd visit–UR/LR periodontal scaling   Code 4342 (specify teeth)

3rd visit–UL/LL periodontal scaling   Code 4342 (specify teeth)

Subsequent recare visits can be coded 4910, periodontal maintenance. Please note that for just a few isolated teeth with 4342, the patient may be maintained with prophylaxis in limited circumstances, in the clinical judgment of the dentist. Some insurance payors will not reimburse 4910 after a single or dual 4342 visit. It is highly variable among companies.

Also, please note that some payors will allow 4342 on the same day as 1110 and some will not.

I can understand why you did not feel that four quadrants of root/planing was warranted for this patient. Most likely, all the periodontally involved teeth can be treated in two visits, with an additional visit for the prophylaxis on the non-periodontally involved teeth. Further, the fee should reflect the amount of time, skill, and expertise needed to treat the patient appropriately. With the information I have provided, you and the doctor should feel confident in treating the early periodontitis patient fairly and appropriately.

Best wishes,

Dianne

Chapter 5

Practice Management

Often, the quality of care in a dental office is influenced, for better or worse, by the way the practice is managed. This includes scheduling, time allotments for specific procedures or patients, staff utilization, procedure coding, and the willingness of every staff member to work as a team toward common goals. Of course, this includes the dentist!

"Schedule Control—The Key to Productivity"

Our schedule often determines our stress level. Scheduling for success involves more than just throwing 10 names on a hygiene schedule and getting through the day the best way you can.

Schedules Gone Awry

Have you looked at your schedule at the beginning of the day and wondered how on earth you were going to survive? Your angst doesn't come from any particular patient's name on the schedule (although everybody has a few 'special' patients that give you a queasy feeling in your stomach when you see their name on the schedule), but rather the sheer number or arrangement of patients. It's no secret that when the schedule is too full, we have to cut corners to stay on time. When there are too many intense procedures, like periodontal scalings in succession, neck and back problems ensue. When too many children are scheduled together, such as several 30-minute appointments in a row, there's not enough time to do everything, keep the operatory turned over, and stay on time for a solo hygienist. What about the 11 a.m. sealant patient? Will there be anyone to help with patient management in keeping a dry field? What about the periodontal maintenance patient scheduled at 12:15 p.m.

who smokes and you KNOW you will need more than 45 minutes to complete. There goes the lunch hour!

Another schedule wrecker is Mrs. Hotshot who is always and forever late. She seems to delight in throwing the schedule into chaos with her tardiness. And what about poor Mr. Lonely who lost his spouse last year and is starving for attention and conversation. It's hard to get anything done and stay on schedule because of his desire to talk. It's also hard NOT to be rude to people like this.

No doubt about it, our schedules cause lots of stress not only for the clinician but also for the person whose job it is to maintain the schedule. The scheduling coordinator leaves the office on Monday evening with a beautifully engineered schedule for Tuesday, only to find it fall apart when she arrives at work the next morning. Now, she has to scramble to find 'warm bodies' to plug the cancellations that have occurred. Further, the re-engineered schedule might not be as beautiful as the original, but rather a patched-up version with people whose needs might not fit the time actually allotted.

Controlling the Schedule

Either the office controls the schedule, or the schedule controls the office. Maintaining control of the schedule means that the scheduling coordinator knows the nuances of how much time clinicians need to do various procedures. Additionally, a good scheduling coordinator knows how to communicate effectively with patients about their appointments.

It is important for clinicians to communicate to scheduling coordinators about time needed for procedures. Scheduling coordinators cannot read the minds of hygienists and dentists, so there must be a communication tool. Many practice management software programs allow clinicians to input the amount of time needed for successive visits. Often there is a default time set for various procedures, such as one hour for quadrant scaling, 30 minutes for a child prophylaxis, etc.

When paper charts are used, there should be a "Treatment Planning" sheet in the chart. This sheet should be a different color and printed on heavy stock paper. This document is the tool that the clinician uses to communicate to the front desk about what kind of appointment the patient will need and how many units of time are necessary. The information should be highlighted in yellow. When the appointment is completed on a later visit, the information is then highlighted in pink, which turns the entry orange. This means it has been completed.

Patient Name_____		Premed yes no	
Date	Tooth	Treatment	Units

Additionally, scheduling coordinators must possess excellent communication skills when talking to patients about their appointments. They should never say, "When would you like to come?" to patients, as this implies the patient can come anytime s/he wants to come. This verbiage is preferred: "The doctor would like to see you as soon as possible for your crown procedure... Fortunately, I have next Tuesday at either 10 a.m. or 2 p.m. Which of those times will work best?" or "Angie would like to see you in three months for your periodontal disease control appointment. Let's find a good time for you."

It is good to give patients a choice of an afternoon or morning time. If a patient requires a 'prime time' appointment, the scheduler should say, "Unfortunately, the first appointment available at that time is six weeks out. But I do have _____." Encourage the patient to accept an alternate time/date. Some patients will be adamant about coming at a particular time of day, so we accommodate our patients as best we can.

All staff members, including the doctor, should eliminate the word 'cleaning' from their vocabulary. This word trivializes the hygiene appointment. Find a word or phrase that better describes the care, such as preventive care, continuing care, or disease control for periodontal maintenance visits. Prime-time appointments—those first thing in the morning and last thing in the evening—are problematic in some offices. I recommend that these appointments not be scheduled more than eight months out (that's two months beyond the traditional six months). These appointment slots are often reserved several months past the six-month mark. Schedule control involves setting limits on how far beyond six months the scheduler is allowed to schedule appointments. For example, Mr. Jones requires a 4 p.m. appointment for his preventive care. All those times are already taken, even up to nine months out (poor schedule control). The verbiage would be, "Unfortunately, there aren't any appointments available at the time you've requested. However, I do have _____ or _____ (something close to when he has requested)." If he is adamant about a particular time, the verbiage would be, "Since nothing is available, we will have to call you when there is a change in the schedule." Another technique is to allow a patient a prime-time appointment on alternating visits in hygiene. This allows more patients who desire a prime-time appointment to get one.

It is more efficient for the hygienist (or the hygiene assistant) to schedule the patient's next visit before the patient leaves the hygiene operatory if there are computers in the clinical area. The hygienist knows the patient's needs and how much time will be needed for the next visit. "Mrs. Smith, your next continuing care visit should be in six months. Would Wednesday, June 15 at 10 a.m. or 2 p.m. be better?" If the patient states she would rather not pre-schedule the appointment, the patient's name should go in a pending file. When an appointment is scheduled, the patient should be given an appointment card with the correct appointment information. Further, the hygienist or assistant should go over the appointment and give the patient a stated reason for the next visit. "When we see you next time, we will be checking that sensitive tooth (or pocket on #30—something in particular for that patient) plus ..."

Confirmation Calls—The Bane of Scheduling Coordinators

Did you know that confirming appointments can actually be counter-productive in some situations? It is true that some patients are annoyed by those calls. In some cases, dependable people do not need to be reminded and can be insulted by the call. Confirmation calls can interrupt something the patient was doing or wake a sleeping child. Sometimes patients will use the opportunity to cancel because we made it easy by calling them.

Actually, I do not know of another profession on earth that goes to the lengths we do to ensure people will come to their appointments! Some offices beg and cajole, almost to the point of harassment. The whole idea of confirmation says, "We're not sure you are coming, so that's why we're bugging you." I think it is entirely possible that patients live DOWN to our expectations!

As an alternative, may I suggest that we start asking patients this question, "Mrs. Johnson, do you require a courtesy confirmation call?" If the patient says no, the scheduling coordinator should say, "Great! I'm going to mark you 'confirmed' right now in my schedule. Thank you for being dependable!" If the patient says yes, inform the patient approximately when s/he will be called. (I recommend placing the call two working days before the scheduled visit.) Here's a good script for a confirmation call:

"Hi, Mrs. Jones. This is Mary at Dr. Smith's office with your courtesy reminder call. Our schedule indicates you have reserved time with our hygienist (or doctor) on Wednesday, May 10 at 9 a.m. We're looking forward to seeing you then!"

Generally, I do not recommend leaving messages asking patients to "call and let us know you got this message," except in the case of a chronic offender, as it is punitive to good patients and ties up business assistants with extraneous telephone calls.

When patients schedule their next six-month visit, the appointment should be verified with the patient. The patient should be told that she will receive a reminder card about 3–4 weeks from the appointment. The person making the appointment should also ask the patient if she would like to have a courtesy reminder call a couple of days from the scheduled visit. If the patient indicates she would like the call, a note should be made for the scheduling coordinator.

One other noteworthy point is that the use of electronic reminders are becoming more and more popular in this day of cell phones and computers. Email reminders and text messaging are excellent methods for reminding people of their appointments when they indicate they prefer this method. Several services are available, such as Televox® (www.televox.com).

Scheduling for Productivity

The scheduling coordinator has a major responsibility to strike a balance between maintaining productivity and keeping clinicians happy. Also, there are variables in the speed at which hygienists and dentists work.

Many hygienists prefer the "1 hour/patient" regimen, because they feel they have adequate time to deliver high-quality care and not feel rushed. In an 8-to-5 day, that would mean a maximum of 7 patients, assuming everyone comes. However, the problem with this scheduling pattern is that there are so many variables with patients. Some need one hour, some only need 40 or 50 minutes, and some need 30 minutes because they have only a few teeth. Some patients might need more time if a periodontal charting and/or radiographs are indicated. Another problem with "1 hour/patient" is that if somebody disappoints, there is a large block of downtime.

Knowing that the most valuable commodity any clinician has is TIME, it is important to use that time wisely. It is recommended that hygienists be proactive in determining how much time will be needed on succeeding visits. For example, if a patient is healthy periodontally and does not require bite wings or periodontal charting on his next visit, that patient should be given an amount of time commensurate with what his needs are, which would be less than if he needed other services. Rather than assigning some arbitrary amount of time for each patient, it would be more prudent and efficient to schedule time based on each individual patient's needs.

A productive schedule is one where there is little or no downtime and a mixture of different procedures that include periodontal scalings or maintenance visits, radiographs, sealants, bleaching trays, prophys, and other adjunctive procedures like fluoride treatments, locally delivered antibiotics or antiseptics, and various products. The industry standard is that one third of hygiene production should be periodontal in nature. However, that may not be the case in some practices. Practices that have a high number of new patients each month typically have more periodontal procedures scheduled. Conversely, those practices that have few new patients also have fewer than 'normal' periodontal procedures.

Rational thinking is that the more patients the hygienist treats, the higher the production will be. However, the most productive procedures, such as periodontal scalings, require longer blocks of time. A hygiene schedule with two (half mouth) periodontal scalings and four prophy patients will be much more productive than a hygiene schedule with nine prophy patients.

Production

4—quadrants RPS @ $200 ea_____	$800
4—prophys @ $80 ea_____	$320
2—BW sets @ $50 ea_____	$100
TOTAL_____	$1,220
9—prophys @ $80 ea_____	$720
4—BW sets @ $50 ea_____	$200
TOTAL_____	$920

Some offices set a production goal for the hygiene department. Goals are good to give the hygienist a target to work toward. However, goals are worthless if attainment or exceeding the goal doesn't result in a reward of some kind. The best way to set a goal is to divide the total production for the past three months by the number of hours worked. This would be an hourly average that could be multiplied by the number of hours worked in a day. The goal should be set a little higher than the average.

Production for past three months—$45,000

Number of hours worked—384

45,000 / 384 = $117/hour average

$117 X 8 hours = 936/average/day

New goal—$1,000/day (6% increase)

Downtime—The Great Profit Destroyer

What is the cost of downtime? To put things into perspective let's consider an example of the high cost of downtime (DT):

Hygienist A—15 min/increment schedule (1 hour has 4 units of time)

Month	DT units	Production	Hours worked
October	215	$19,513	155

$19,513/ 155 = $126/hour production

$126 / 4 (number of units in 1 hour) = $31.50 (1 time unit of production)

$31.50 X 215 (DT units) = $6,772.50

$6,772.50 (DT cost for October)

You can easily see how costly downtime is for a dental practice. If we assumed the amount for October was typical and multiplied the downtime cost in our example—which was for one month only—by 12, the cost for the year would be $81,270! Additionally, this example does not take into account the hygienist's wages, which is an expense as well.

Causes for too much downtime can include:

■ Weak verbal skills in scheduling/confirmation protocol.

■ Patients not being held responsible for their appointments.

■ Not enough patients in the practice or mass exodus of patients from the practice.

■ Poorly trained or inefficient business assistants who are not focused on the number one priority of keeping the schedule full.

Tips for Productive Scheduling

An over-booked schedule will cause the hygienist to cut corners and quality of care delivered in an effort to stay on time, and an under-booked schedule results in low profit margins for the practice. Patient appointment times should reflect the appropriate amount of time needed to deliver high-quality care while being efficient and productive.

■ Do not schedule more than two intense procedures back to back.

■ Do not schedule more than three 30-minute appointments consecutively unless there is a dedicated hygiene assistant.

■ Schedule 20 minutes of flex time before lunch and at day's end.

■ Identify chronically late patients by stating their appointment time 15 minutes earlier than the scheduled time.

■ Patients who have proven to be unreliable by their history of disappointment should not be allowed to pre-schedule their six-month appointment. Rather, such patients should receive reminder cards that instruct them to call for an appointment.

- When pre-scheduling patients six months out, do not completely fill days with appointments. Leave some scattered openings, and block off one day toward the end of the month as a 'safety net' day in case patients have to be reappointed because of hygienist absence. If no absence occurs, the day can be appointed with patients who telephone for an appointment.

- Block periodontal scaling time in the schedule to be sure the periodontal patients are seen in a timely manner consistent with treating an infection. To know how much time to block, go back three months and total the number of periodontal appointments used. Divide this number into the total days worked. This will be the average number of periodontal appointments needed on a daily basis.

- When a patient is late, seat that patient and do what you can with the time that is left. Prioritize what is most important and postpone procedures that can be done on a succeeding visit. However, do not feel you have to do everything you had originally planned to do with only a fraction of the time needed.

- Communicate with the scheduling coordinator about time needed for individual patients. Understand that scheduling coordinators have a difficult task trying to keep both patients and clinicians satisfied.

- The most productive schedules have a variety of procedures scheduled, including periodontal procedures.

- Confirmation calls should be called "courtesy reminder calls," and patients should be asked if they need or 'require' such a call.

- Downtime destroys profitability. Keep downtime to a minimum, and track the unscheduled units of time each month to figure the true downtime cost.

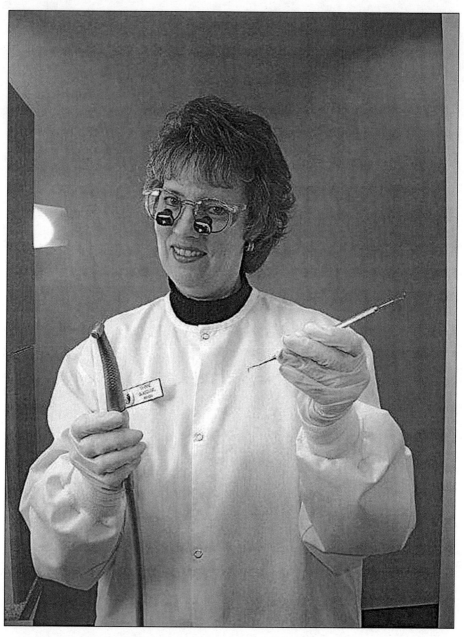

Dianne with her Designs for Vision® loupes.

The Consummate Dental Hygienist

"Waiting for the Doctor"

Dear Dianne,

I have been a dental hygienist for over 20 years. Recently, I relocated to a different city and found a position in a very upscale group practice. There are six general dentists, four specialists, and six hygienists. The office is beautiful and has very nice equipment, I am well paid, and I feel I have integrated well into the practice. Sounds great, right? So what could be my problem?

The problem is having my schedule wrecked almost daily from having to wait excessively long for the doctor to come and check my patients. Twice this week, I have left the office in tears at the end of the day from the stress of running behind schedule. It is common for me to be a full patient behind schedule. I'm the last one to clock out, and the office manager is questioning why it's taking me so long. I have never worked in a practice where I feel so disrespected by the doctors. Plus, I don't like making my patients angry. I feel like I am always apologizing for keeping them waiting. Recently, one of my female patients had to wait 30 minutes on her exam. When the doctor came in the room, she blasted the doctor for making her wait and ruining my schedule. I have never worked in any office where getting the doctor to check my patient was a problem, and my current problem is stressing me to the max! I am normally very prompt. What can I do to get the doctor to come and check my patients so I can stay on schedule?

Brenda, RDH

Dear Brenda,

I can feel your pain! I, too, am a very prompt person, and running late for anything is a major source of stress for me. Without a doubt, the number one complaint that I receive from hygienists is running behind schedule because of having to wait excessively long for a doctor exam. You are not alone in your frustration.

Consider the doctor's position. In some practices, the doctor is scheduled so heavily that there is NO time in the schedule for hygiene exams. I've witnessed doctors literally running down the hallway to do a hygiene exam. In one such practice where I consulted, the doctor told me that keeping hygiene checked was THE most stressful part of his day. Consider what it would be like if you had to get up from every patient and go do something else.

There are two issues to consider: (1) schedule control and (2) best time to summon the doctor. The primary problem causing your dilemma is poor schedule control. Simply put, there is no time in the doctor's schedule to examine your patients in a prompt manner. If you have 10 patients and it takes five minutes to perform a hygiene check, that's 50 minutes. In many doctor schedules, there's not even five minutes extra, much less 50. Even with a "normal" schedule, treatment does not always progress the way it was originally scheduled. Sometimes procedures take longer than expected.

While scheduling is a front desk function, the business assistants usually schedule according to the time requested by the doctor. Some doctors do not allow themselves enough time for procedures. For example, a doctor may feel he can do a 3-surface composite in 40 minutes, but the reality is that it always takes 50 minutes. Being too conservative on time allowance causes log jams in the doctor's schedule, which spills over to your schedule.

There may be a logistical problem as well, particularly if your building is large and your operatory is not close to the doctor's operatories. When the doctor has to walk a long distance to your operatory, the distance adds to the time issue.

The second problem is the timing of the doctor summons. In many practices, the hygienist will wait until she or he is completely finished with the patient before summoning the doctor. If the hygienist uses all or almost all the scheduled appointment time, waiting until the end to summon the doctor will guarantee the hygienist to run behind. You finish your patient, you summon the doctor, and then you wait...and wait...and wait. You feel bad if you leave the patient alone in the operatory, but eventually you run out of small talk and the awkwardness of 'dead air' envelopes the operatory. "The doctor will be here shortly," you say as you offer the patient a magazine he or she does not want, while you pace the hallway and tap on your watch face. You can feel the tension building with each passing minute, and by the time the doctor arrives, you're 10 minutes into the next patient's time. It takes another 10 minutes to complete the check, dismiss the patient, turn over the room, and seat the next patient, who, by the way, has been waiting in the reception room 20 minutes. Nobody wins when you wait until you are finished to summon the doctor.

Here is what I recommend. Speak with the doctor privately and tell him that you desire to treat the patients with excellence, efficiency, and most of all, **respect.** Tell him you understand that he is not keeping you and your patients waiting on purpose, that his schedule is the problem. Ask him to consider your dilemma and the **disrespect** being shown patients by making them wait excessively. Ask if it is possible to lighten his schedule slightly so to allow time for timely hygiene exams.

Further, I would ask you not to wait until you are finished to summon the doctor. Incorporate an "interrupted exam" protocol. The sequence is:

- Greet and seat the patient.
- Update medical history
- Take blood pressure reading
- Do a tour of the mouth
- Take any necessary radiographs
- Perform any necessary chartings
- Summon the doctor

This gives the doctor 20–30 minutes to get to your operatory for the exam. Other than a chairside emergency, I know of no valid reason that a doctor would keep a hygienist waiting longer than that. If the patient has a heavy build-up of soft debris, polish first so the doctor will have an unimpeded view of the teeth. When the doctor appears in the doorway, say to your patient, "Oh look, here's Dr. XX. I'm going to stop long enough for him to check you, and then we'll finish up."

Unfortunately, most people do not like going to the dentist. They know we use sharp, pointed instruments and needles in their mouths. Many have had painful, unpleasant dental experiences in the past, and they walk in our doors unhappy that they even have to be there. It seems the least we can do is be prompt and not show disrespect to them by keeping them waiting an inordinate amount of time. Their time is just as important as our time. If we disrespect their time, they will disrespect our time by being late or breaking appointments.

The fact that one of your patients recently admonished the doctor for the long wait should have been a wake-up call. Let's hope he is amenable to improving his schedule and changing the exam protocol before he loses patients from the practice. After all, good customer service is important!

Best wishes,

Dianne

"The High Cost of Downtime"

Dear Dianne,

I've been doing hygiene for almost 20 years, and I've worked in several different offices. However, I have never worked with a doctor who frets over openings in the schedule as much as my current employer. He gets visibly upset if I don't have a patient in my chair. My operatory is at the end of the hall, and he makes numerous trips just to peek in the door to see what I'm doing. Once, I was in the restroom, and he knocked on the door and asked if I was in there! I was shocked and embarrassed!

I should mention that we've had difficulty keeping the schedule full during the past year. The unfilled openings in my schedule appear to coincide with the hiring of a new front desk assistant. The former assistant was very good at keeping my schedule full, and rarely did I have unfilled time. Now I average at least two openings every day in my schedule, and I've had a few days that literally fell apart. Normally I see about nine patients per day, but there have been days where I only saw three or four patients all day. Our front desk assistants always appear busy, but sometimes I wonder what they are really doing.

I feel like I'm under the doctor's microscope, and his anxiety over my schedule is making me a nervous wreck! I've been in this office four years, but I've come to the place where I dread going to work. For some reason, I'm made to feel guilty when my schedule is not full. I want to shout "IT'S NOT MY FAULT!"

Short of leaving, is there anything I can do to get the doctor off my back?

Feeling the Pressure

Dear Feeling,

Being the object of someone's constant scrutiny is uncomfortable and nerve racking, and I would not want to trade places with you!

It is obvious there is a problem at the front desk, and I suspect the new assistant was not trained properly when she was hired. Sometimes, new business assistants are thrown into positions with little or NO training and no job description, but are expected to perform like seasoned professionals. Plus, new assistants do not know the patients and the many nuances involved in working with a particular patient base.

In consulting, I've worked with many different front desk assistants over the years. I've seen superstars and slackers, and many mediocre performers. However, the best ones are those individuals with a clear understanding of the priorities of their position and a strong work ethic. In fact, practice profitability rests on a business assistant's ability and willingness to do his/her job well. It sounds like the former assistant in your office was a 'go-getter' who took her job seriously and understood that her primary responsibility was keeping clinical people busy.

At the front desk, there are two *primary* responsibilities—scheduling and financial management. Typically, one person is the scheduling coordinator and another person is the financial coordinator. There needs to be clear and concise job descriptions for each position, and the doctor should hold business assistants accountable for the performance of their particular positions. Fortunately, each assistant's efficiency can be (at least partially) measured in a number. For the financial assistant, that number would be the collections percentage of adjusted production. That number should be 98% or better. For scheduling coordinators, the number is downtime percentage of total available time for various clinicians. In order to measure downtime percentage, downtime has to be tracked. We like to see downtime at 5% or less.

The doctor would do well to redirect his anxiety over your schedule to those responsible for maintaining the schedule. He's not seeing the big picture. All he knows is that your wages are significantly higher than what the business assistants receive, and he's stressing over your pay in the face of low production. If you are salaried, you get paid no matter what you produce, so there's no incentive to be mindful of production. If you are commissioned, your pay would depend on what you produce, which puts more pressure on you and the business assistant to keep you busy.

Causes for too much downtime can include:

1. Weak verbal skills in scheduling/confirmation protocol

2. Patients not being held responsible for their appointments

3. Not enough patients in the practice or mass exodus of patients from the practice

4. Poorly trained or inefficient business assistants who are not focused on the number one priority of keeping the schedule full

I'd be willing to bet the doctor never conducts performance appraisals and probably doesn't have job descriptions for each position. He needs some outside help with business management with a focus on training for the front desk assistants.

I advise you to start tracking your downtime, and someone should track the doctor's downtime as well. I also advise you to request a conference with the doctor about your concerns. Use your thinking skills to develop some strategies for correcting this problem. Try to open up communication and show him that you are as concerned about your schedule as he is. However, until your front desk problems are addressed, I do not see this situation improving very much.

Skill and expertise aside, the most valuable commodity for any clinician is TIME. Time is money in many professions, especially dentistry. Learning to manage time, schedule appropriately, keep clinicians busy and happy, and still maintain grace and tact is the challenge business assistants face every day. It is also the key to practice financial health and profitability. Is anything more important than that?

Best wishes,

Dianne

"Over-Scheduling and Quality of Care"

Dear Dianne,

I have worked in the dental profession for 11 years now, first as an Expanded Functions Dental Assistant (EFDA) and now as an RDH. There are very few jobs available in my area. In fact, some the women I graduated with three years ago are still looking.

Recently I accepted a full-time position in a general practice setting with a less-than-attractive dental hygiene department. Scheduling is set on a 30-minute schedule, and when the dental assistants are available, they sometimes help take radiographs and tear down rooms. Often I feel I am short-changing my patients. I feel ashamed that I have accepted a position like this, because I promised myself I would never do assembly-line hygiene! But, as a provider for my family, at this point, I have no other options.

I have made suggestions about adjusting the schedule, but my suggestions have been blown off. In fact, the Officer Manager (the dentist's wife) said, "It's OK if you run behind. We will just contact the next patient and move that person down." Totally not my point! She told me that I should never look at the clock and always use as much time as I need. However, this does not seem like ideal practice management to me. When I make notations that I need 45 minutes for the next visit, my requests are ignored. HELP!!!

As an intelligent and skilled professional, I am shorting my patients from receiving optimal care and putting myself at risk by skirting established standards of care. My question is this: What facts and information can I gather and provide to the husband-and-wife team to encourage at least 40-minute prophylaxis appointments with the help of a full-time assistant?

Overworked and discouraged

Dear Overworked,

Your letter touched my heart, and I ache for you! You are working in a 'prophy mill' that is not unlike the notorious 'puppy mills' where the mantra is quantity over quality. Puppy mills breed their dogs to death just to turn out more puppies to sell. By over-breeding, they injure their dogs, some to the point of death. By over-scheduling, hygienists are made to feel the work they do is not important. Many are injured from repetitive motion injuries associated with over-scheduling. Some good clinicians leave the profession as they burn out from the stress of daily over-scheduling.

The suggestion to ignore the clock shows a blatant disrespect for the patient's time and your own sanity!

Is the practice heavily into HMO/PPO dentistry? If it is, the practice cannot charge out the full fee, so often appointments are shortened to allow for more volume, which theoretically makes up for the shortfall in fees. I'm not making excuses here, just explaining the economics of the issue. However, insurance participation or not, there is no excuse for substandard care of our patients.

My first question: Does the wife overbook her husband, the dentist? What would happen if she did? Obviously, she couldn't get away with that. How would the doctor like it if he knew he had to cut corners out of necessity? How would he like it if he TOLD the scheduler he needed 45 minutes for a procedure and was given only 30 minutes? What if this over-scheduling scenario happened every day, not just once in awhile? Most likely, there would be hell to pay!

My next question is this: Are there two hygiene rooms available? If so, you could do assisted hygiene with a dedicated assistant, see 12 to 14 patients in an 8-to-5 day, and be less tired at day's end than if you saw nine patients in a solo model. I worked an assisted model and much preferred it over solo hygiene. I found the assisted model to be much more relaxed for me since I did not have to attend to clean up, set up, sterilization, dismissal of the patient, or scheduling of the next appointment. A big plus was having the benefit of someone to help me with chartings and chairside assistance if I needed an extra set of hands. You would be amazed how expeditiously you can complete periodontal scaling if you have someone to suction for you while power scaling.

If assisted hygiene is not an option because of insufficient number of available treatment rooms, then you have some choices:

1. Consider moving. Some areas of the country have become saturated with hygienists to the point where jobs are scarce. Apparently, there are more doctors retiring than new graduates to take over their practices. Additionally, over the past 15 years, new hygiene programs have sprung up all over the country, the result being over-saturation of the job market. However, there are areas where the hygiene market is not

saturated. If moving is an option, be sure to contact the state dental hygiene association to get information about job availability.

2. Put your thoughts down on paper and approach the doctor and office manager with the problem and a viable solution, part of which is to schedule your own patients for their successive appointments. Appeal to their sense of fairness and professional pride. "If you went to a doctor for an outpatient procedure, the doctor indicated he needed one hour, but his scheduler only gave him 45 minutes, what part of your procedure would you want him to cut corners on? That's the predicament I'm in. I can't possibly do what I know I should be doing in the small time I'm given. I feel like I'm cheating the patients, and the guilt is killing me. I really need your help on this. I don't think our patients are stupid, and they cannot possibly perceive high-quality care the way they are rushed in and out. These are YOUR patients. I want to take good care of them, but that takes TIME."

The office administrator has never walked in your shoes, so she has no way of understanding your dilemma unless you use an analogy she can understand. The right communication could turn this situation around for you, and for the sake of the patients and you, I hope it does. The standards of care of dentistry and dental hygiene that are set forth by licensing boards are not to be ignored in the pursuit of higher profits. To do so is to put our patients and licenses at risk.

The sad fact is, you are not alone in this over-scheduling dilemma. Schedule abuse and low-quality care exist when the leader is more interested in quantity over quality. I maintain that patients are not stupid. If they do not receive high-quality care, they will not place high value on the preventive care they are given. And if they do not perceive high value, they are not likely to continue that care if they have to pay out of pocket, which is a growing problem for more and more people as they lose their jobs and dental benefits. What goes around comes around.

Best wishes,

Diane

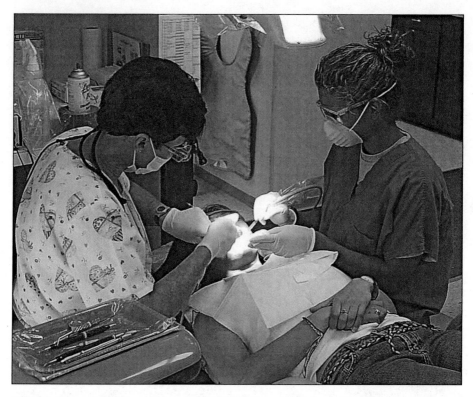

Shirley Cross, RDH, working with Erika Guzman, dental hygiene assistant.

"The Dental Hygiene Assistant— the Hygienist's Strong Right Arm!"

With the passing of time, business models change. The admonition to "work smarter, not harder" should be the goal of every progressive business owner. However, change is difficult for many people. We get in a rut of doing things the way we have always done them, and we are sometimes reluctant to step out of our comfort zone.

Incorporating more efficient work practices is important in keeping the hygiene department profitable. Simply working faster and seeing more patients is not the answer. Working the traditional 'solo' dental hygiene model is inefficient, in that the hygienist has to spend a large part of his/her day performing tasks that could be done by an auxiliary. For example, operatory tear down and set up takes about eight minutes per patient. If the hygienist sees an average of eight people per day, operatory turnover alone is one full hour, or **one full hour** that another patient could be seen.

Additionally, many tasks that should be a part of every dental hygiene visit are often omitted because of lack of time. A good example is routine blood pressure screening. Periodontal probing takes at least twice as long to do without an assistant to record probing depths as it does with an assistant. Meaningful conversation about home care procedures and needed dentistry is another area that often goes lacking. Even necessary radiographs are omitted or postponed until the next visit when time is short.

Scheduling Inefficiency

The one-hour-per-patient model of scheduling in hygiene is inefficient. While some patients do need a full hour, the fact is that patients are quite variable in their preventive care needs. The patient with immaculate home care does not require the same amount of time as a patient with poor home care. The patient with a partial dentition does not generally require the same amount of time as a patient with a full dentition. Smokers may require more time than non-smokers. Children certainly do not require one hour for a prophylaxis and adjunctive services.

	Hygienist	Assistant
Set up operatory		5
Review patient record	1	
Seat patient and greet patient		2-4
Take blood pressure		1
Review medical history		3
Oral cancer screening and head and neck exam	2-3	
Expose any necessary radiographs		5
Inquire about dental concerns	1-2	
Plaque control and oral hygiene instructions		5-15
Discuss dental needs	5-10	
Periodontal charting	5-10	
Prophylaxis	20-30	
Signal and wait for doctor		5-15
Dispense oral hygiene aids		1
Record areas of caries or other pathology	2	
Relate concerns to doctor		2
Make patient's next appointment		5
Document in patient chart (computer) all observations, patient comments, and future treatment recommended		5
Dismiss patient		2
Perform aseptic techniques in operatory, prepare instruments for sterilization		5-15
Set up operatory for next patient		5

A better model would be to assign time based on the patient's needs. Each patient should be evaluated objectively and scheduled accordingly. After patients become established in the practice, their pattern of home care becomes evident.

When a practice hires a hygiene assistant but does not change the way hygiene is scheduled, the assistant is not utilized to the fullest. If scheduling is not changed, there will be no increase in production. The assistant only serves to assist in clean-up, developing radiographs, and other menial duties.

A much better business model for the hygiene department is to use two operatories and a dedicated assistant. By incorporating such a model, the hygienist is free to do those procedures that only a licensed hygienist can do. Other delegable procedures, such as operatory turnover, are assigned to a dedicated assistant. Opposite is a list of procedures that take place in a typical dental hygiene appointment and the appropriate personnel to perform each task.

While these times are not absolutes, it is easy to see that there are many aspects of the dental hygiene appointment that can be handled by a qualified assistant. This frees the hygienist to move to another operatory and continue to see patients. The hygienist can focus on doing those things that only a licensed hygienist can do. The person who benefits the most is the patient, because the quality of care is better when the hygienist can focus on providing quality treatment.

Of course, for this model to be workable, two operatories must be available for the hygienist.

The hygienist would work much like many dentists work by rotating between operatories. While the assistant is preparing operatory 1, the hygienist is in operatory 2 seeing a patient. The dental assistant would not necessarily have to be in the operatory with the hygienist but should be available as needed. Times when the assistant would be needed directly with the hygienist would be to record examination findings or periodontal probings, to provide water evacuation during ultrasonic scaler use, or to provide assistance with placing sealants.

Productivity

Hygienist without an assistant

Assume one patient/hour and a 32-hour week, two cancellations, hourly pay at $25/hour

Average cost of dental hygiene appointment, $85 (excluding doctor exam)

32 patients X $85 =	$2,720
Subtract 2 cancellations	(170)
TOTAL	$2,550
Subtract salary	(800)
Subtract benefits (20%)	(160)
GROSS PROFIT	$1,590

Hygienist with an assistant

Assume one patient per 40 minutes, 32-hour week, four cancellations Assistant salary @$12/hour

48 patients X $85 =	$4,080
Subtract 4 cancellations	(340)
TOTAL	$3,740
Subtract hygienist salary	(800)
Subtract assistant salary	(384)
Subtract benefits (20%)	(236)
GROSS PROFIT	$2,320

Hygienists who work with assistants report that doing hygiene procedures is more enjoyable than working solo. Additionally, one of the biggest time wasters—waiting on the doctor for a hygiene exam—is eliminated. The hygienist can move on to the next patient while the assistant waits with the patient for the doctor.

Disadvantages

The disadvantage of working with a dedicated assistant is evident when the assistant is absent. An assisted schedule is impossible to work without an assistant. Therefore, the schedule must be re-engineered if the assistant is absent and a temporary assistant cannot be located. It is recommended that a **written** protocol be established for the dental hygiene assistant that specifies exactly how the operatory is to be set up, exactly what tasks he/she is responsible for performing, and other pertinent information related to the job. Having a written protocol makes it easier for a new trainee to learn the job.

Another disadvantage is in having an assistant who is not organized and efficient. It is the assistant's responsibility to keep patient flow smooth in the hygiene department and to be available to help the hygienist when needed. It is essential to have a person who knows what her job expectations are and shows responsibility in meeting those expectations.

Additionally, the mindset of the hygienist working with an assistant must be one of teamwork and equality. The hygienist must view this person as his/her 'strong right arm' and treat the assistant with respect, not as an underling.

Final Thought

The key to working effectively with assisted hygiene is to begin gradually. Following the hiring and training period, begin integrating with a half day, then a full day. Allow for a learning curve. Do not be deterred if a day falls apart or things do not flow smoothly initially. In dentistry, we are such perfectionists that we often do not give ourselves the time we need to learn or try a new mode of operating.

Careful planning and appropriate implementation of the assisted hygiene model can open a whole new world of opportunity in the practice. Having a dedicated hygiene assistant allows the hygienist to see more patients, provide better care, and work more efficiently. It is an especially attractive option for areas where shortages of qualified hygienists exist. Patients often perceive a higher level of service when they are not left in the operatory alone. Time with the patient can be used to the fullest by providing more one-on-one contact with members of the dental team. Assisted hygiene is a triple winner for the patient, the hygienist, and the practice!

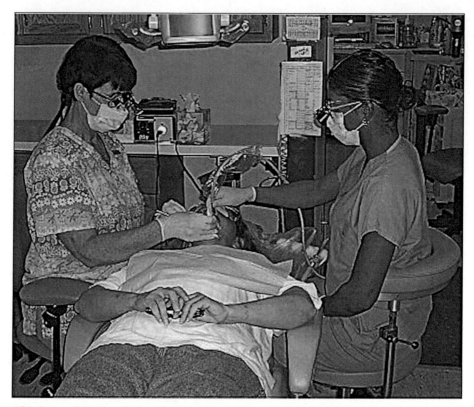

Shirley and Erika demonstrate proper assisted hygiene technique.

The Consummate Dental Hygienist

"The Sabotage of Assisted Hygiene"

Working in an assisted hygiene model can be productive, professionally gratifying, and fun. However, the model can be sabotaged if any of the four essential ingredients for success are missing.

In order to implement assisted hygiene in any practice, there are four prerequisites that have to be satisfied. First, there must be two operatories that are completely equipped with power scalers, instruments, and anything else that is needed to provide hygiene services. The second prerequisite is that there must be a dedicated assistant who works with the hygienist exclusively. The third requirement is an understanding of how to engineer an assisted schedule. Finally, the model must be embraced by everyone involved with a dedication to make it work.

Sabotage #1

When Dr. Davis heard a speaker describe how much more productive the assisted model of hygiene was than solo hygiene, he made the decision to give it a try in his practice. He had three total operatories in his office—one hygiene operatory and two operatories equipped for restorative procedures. One of the restorative operatories was used primarily as an overflow treatment room, so Dr. Davis reasoned it could be used by both he and the hygienist as needed. The doctor reasoned that the hygienist could place her power scaler on a rolling cart and move it from room to room as needed, as he did not wish to invest in an additional power scaler.

The first day of assisted hygiene was a disaster, and Dr. Davis's hygienist was near tears by the end of the day. She felt exhausted from the rigors of constantly moving the power scaler, instruments, and everything else she needed. The second operatory was simply too small to function as both a restorative and hygiene operatory. At one point, Dr. Davis's assistant had placed one of his 'overflow' patients in the second operatory, which left no room for the hygienist's patient who was scheduled to be seated in the same treatment room. This caused the hygienist to run behind the remainder of the day.

The assisted model of hygiene in Dr. Davis's office was doomed from the start by violating the first principle, which is providing two completely equipped, mirrored hygiene operatories. The doctor put his hygienist in a stressful, uncomfortable position by asking her to work in a treatment room not set up for hygiene procedures. Asking clinicians to move necessary equipment back and forth between treatment rooms is burdensome and frustrating! Most likely, the hygienist will resist any future efforts to practice assisted hygiene because of this initial bad experience.

Sabotage #2

Dr. Moore's practice experienced a decrease in demand which made it difficult to keep two full-time hygienists busy. So when one hygienist decided to retire, Dr. Moore decided to implement assisted hygiene rather than hire another hygienist. He hired an additional assistant to work with the hygienist, and her duties were delineated in a written job description. The hygienist and assistant learned to work together, and the hygienist found she was less tired at the end of the day compared to when she worked solo. The hygienist enjoyed having help with periodontal charting, suctioning, and all the other duties her assistant performed, such as room set-up and turnover. The greatest advantage was the increased production. The hygienist was able to increase from an average of eight patients per day to 12 patients, which increased her production by about 45%.

However, the assisted hygiene model began to crumble when the hygiene assistant noticed she was being pulled from her hygiene duties to help the doctor or his assistant on a fairly regular basis. It seems when the doctor hired the hygiene assistant, he told her that her primary duty would be to assist the hygienist, but she would also be required to help with restorative procedures from time to time as well. Dr. Moore did not understand that requiring the hygiene assistant to function in two roles was a prescription for failure.

The only time the hygiene assistant should be expected to help in other departments is if there is downtime in the hygiene schedule due to an occasional cancellation or no-show. A hygienist cannot work an assisted model alone. Dr. Moore should consider how frustrated he would be if his assistant was absent when he needed her, only to be found helping in another part of the practice.

Dr. Moore's hygienist became disillusioned and frustrated because of increasing demands on her assistant by other staff members. The hygiene assistant felt stressed and overworked from being pulled in two directions. Friction developed between the hygienist and assistant as a result of stress on the hygienist to perform her duties and the assistant duties when the assistant was pulled away. So when the assistant resigned, the assisted model was abandoned.

Evidently, Dr. Moore did not respect the role of the assistant to the hygienist in an assisted hygiene model. The assistant functions as the hygienist's strong right arm in maintaining flow, staying on time, keeping treatment areas ready, dismissing patients, scheduling future appointments, taking radiographs, and sterilizing instruments. Further, the problems experienced by the hygienist in not having her assistant available when needed have (most likely) jaded her against assisted hygiene.

Sabotage #3

Dr. Cathcart decided to implement assisted hygiene to meet rising demand for hygiene services in his practice. Hygienists were in short supply in his area, so assisted hygiene seemed like a good solution.

He had four operatories—two restorative operatories, one hygiene operatory, and one 'junk' room that was plumbed and ready for upfitting. With his hygienist's help, he ordered the necessary equipment and instruments and hired a hygiene assistant.

The scheduling coordinator did not fully understand how to schedule for assisted hygiene. She was told to "stagger the schedule every 30 minutes or so." Before implementing assisted hygiene, the hygienist was accustomed to seeing about nine patients per day. On the 'launch' day, however, there were 16 patients scheduled! When the hygienist saw the schedule, she nearly panicked! How on earth could she be expected to nearly double the number of patients she saw and still provide high-quality care?

As expected, the first day was stressful from being over-scheduled. The hygienist worked well into her lunch hour and nearly an hour over at day's end. She was so tired and frustrated after the first day that she felt like resigning.

A little common sense regarding appropriate scheduling would have been helpful. The best advice is to start slowly and gradually build as the hygienist and assistant learn how to work in tandem. If the hygienist is accustomed to seeing eight patients per day, the first assisted day should have no more than 11 patients. As the protocol becomes established, the hygienist can eventually see a few more patients. However, depending on the patient mix, an assisted schedule (in an 8-to-5 day) will typically max out at about 12 to 13 patients (possibly more if there are several children in the mix). Obviously, a highly qualified assistant can perform more duties, such as exposing radiographs and polishing. With an untrained assistant, the hygienist will have to perform many duties that could be delegated to an assistant with the appropriate credentials.

Sabotage #4

Carol, the scheduling coordinator, was not happy when the doctor announced that he wanted to implement assisted hygiene in the practice. She was vocal in her opposition at the staff meeting, and stated she did not see how it could possibly work. Carol did not like the idea of hiring an additional assistant, and she felt her job would be complicated by increasing the number of patients seen by the hygienist. Carol did not like change—period.

The assistant hired to help the hygienist was inexperienced but willing to learn. Nevertheless, Carol projected a less-than-friendly attitude. The young assistant was intimidated by the scheduling coordinator, and when a job came open in a nearby office, she resigned. The schedule was thrown into turmoil, and it seemed the only alternative was to go back to solo hygiene. Carol was secretly happy to return to the old familiar routine.

In this situation, the doctor was partly to blame for the failure of the assisted model because he was not enthusiastically committed to making the model work. He allowed his scheduling coordinator to sabotage the model through her negative remarks and passive-aggressive attitude. If the doctor had provided more support and provided the scheduling coordinator with encouragement and direction, the model would have had a better chance of thriving.

Avoid the Sabotage

Assisted hygiene can be a win-win-win situation for hygienists, patients, and the practice if it is not sabotaged by any of the scenarios outlined above. Hygienists who practice assisted hygiene overwhelmingly report a more relaxed work environment by having a dedicated assistant. Patients are provided comprehensive care from the hygienist and a well-trained assistant. Additionally, the practice benefits through increased production in the hygiene department. *(See Appendix A for a sample Assisted Schedule.)*

The Consummate Dental Hygienist

"The Patient with Mild Periodontitis"

Dear Dianne,

The business office where I work seems confused about how to code the patient with gingivitis or early periodontitis. Since insurance coding is not my 'cup of tea,' can you provide some direction that will help them understand why it is not appropriate to use periodontal codes for gingivitis patients? Also, what treatment protocol do you suggest for the early periodontitis patient?

Tar Heel Hygienist

Dear Tar Heel,

It is unfortunate that the ADA Code Committee has not seen a need to provide any specific gingivitis codes. From experience, we know gingivitis can range from mild to quite severe. A patient who has not had professional care for an extended length of time is likely to present with some level of gingivitis and/or periodontitis. Many dental hygienists experience high stress when patients present with significant deposits and insufficient time to complete the whole mouth in one visit.

Let's take Joe Blow. He has not been in for three years, but he is on your schedule today. The previous hygienist noted heavy deposits and staining—yes, he is a smoker. Your assessment and radiographs do not reveal any bone loss, but there is heavy calculus and staining. And you only have 40 minutes. After the assessments and radiographs, you only have 20 minutes, and you know there is no way for you to be thorough in one visit. Joe's treatment will need to be phased.

My suggestion is to concentrate your efforts on one side of the mouth only. Your patient is more likely to return if you refrain from doing a 'drive-by scaling' and remove all the gross debris with your power scaler. There are three options for codes:

D4355—debridement to enable diagnosis. This is my least favorite code, as most insurance plans will not recognize it and typically deny it. However, some offices tell me they use it and get reimbursed.

D1110—prophylaxis. Outside PPO/HMO dentistry, it is appropriate to adjust the fee upward to reflect the degree of severity.

D4999—unspecified periodontal procedure by report. This code requires a narrative such as: "Patient has had no care for three years. Heavy debris/staining, gingivitis, but no pocketing evident. Will need additional visit to complete." Some insurance companies will pay on this code, some will not. It is variable. Submitting a picture taken with your intraoral camera might help.

The second visit to complete the gingivitis patient will be appropriately coded D1110. The advantage of using D4999 on the first visit is that the patient should still have benefits six months down the road, as most plans allow two preventive appointments per year. However, keep in mind that insurance companies have the option to remap the code to D1110 if they choose, which means the patient will have to pay out of pocket in six months if he returns for preventive care. Additionally, some companies require that there be a minimum of six months between preventive visits. If that is the case, the patient may have to pay out of pocket for one of the visits needed initially.

Look at the situation like this: No one forced the patient to abandon care or neglect his teeth for an extended time, which resulted in the need for an additional visit. Therefore, the business office assistant should have no problem relating the necessity for out-of-pocket payment for care. Why do we think we have to do whatever is necessary to ensure patients do not incur out-of-pocket expense? Could it be that we are part of the problem of patients who have totally abdicated their responsibility for payment for dental services? I think so.

It is imperative that your business office NOT use periodontal codes for patients with no periodontal disease. This is called 'upcoding' and is blatantly illegal. Another example of upcoding is charging for a surgical extraction when the extraction was simple. Unfortunately, there have been far too many dental professionals that thought they could fly under the radar and use inappropriate codes for procedures. When their fraud is discovered, the penalties can result in astronomical fines and/or license suspension or revocation and even jail time. Dentists and dental hygienists have been found guilty of insurance fraud in the past.

The patient with mild periodontitis presents a different treatment dilemma with regard to coding. Let's say John presents with pocketing that is 5 mm or more on two teeth in each arch. John does not qualify for quadrant scaling. He needs at least four teeth in the arch that are periodontally involved to qualify for D4341, quadrant scaling. However, he does qualify for D4342, root planing and scaling on one to three teeth. Your treatment sequence should be:

1st visit—prophylaxis for non-periodontally involved teeth	Code 1110
2nd visit—UR/LR periodontal scaling (specify teeth)	Code 4342
3rd visit—UL/LL periodontal scaling (specify teeth)	Code 4342

Subsequent recare visits can be coded D4910, periodontal maintenance. Please note that for just a few isolated teeth with D4342, the patient may be maintained with prophylaxis in limited circumstances, in the clinical judgment of the dentist. Some insurance payors will not reimburse 4910 after a single or dual D4342 visit. It is highly variable among companies. Also, please note that some payors will allow D4342 on the same day as D1110 and some will not. Again, this is highly variable.

Allow me to recommend an excellent source of insurance coding information to assist your business assistants with insurance coding questions. Dr. Charles Blair publishes a coding manual called *Coding with Confidence: the 'Go To' Dental Insurance Guide.* This resource can be ordered from www.drcharlesblair.com. This manual would be a wise investment for the practice.

The point I wish to make is this: Use the correct code for what you do. If the service you provide is a prophylaxis, then code the procedure D1110. If the service you provide is periodontal therapy or maintenance, then use the appropriate codes—D4341, D4342, or D4910. If all you provide is a debridement, use D4355. Use code D4999 to delineate specific procedures that do not fit into the other categories. If the patient qualifies for dental benefits, fine. If not, then that is not your problem. All the same, the bill has to be paid if services are provided. Using improper codes is illegal, immoral, and unethical. Don't do it!

Best wishes,

Dianne

Chapter 6

Legal Considerations

It seems clinicians have enough to think about in providing high-quality care to their patients. It's true, you do, but it may not be enough to keep you out of a courtroom. In today's litigious society, dental professionals must be aware of and comply with certain legal requirements if they would avoid potentially career-ending lawsuits. Even if you do everything right you may still be sued, therefore it is important to protect yourself. Another area to be aware of is employers who take unfair advantage of you. Know what they can and cannot legally expect of you. The law cannot protect you if you are unaware of its precepts.

"Prevention vs. Prosecution— Malpractice and the Dental Hygienist"

Malpractice. The very word strikes fear in the hearts and minds of all healthcare providers. In fact, according to risk management statistics, every dentist can expect at least one malpractice lawsuit in his or her practice lifetime. What about dental hygienists? Are they at risk? Should dental hygienists invest in their own malpractice insurance? Read on to learn of the unpleasant circumstances surrounding four dental hygienists.

Limits of Malpractice Coverage

Carol practiced dental hygiene for 25 years without carrying malpractice insurance. She reasoned that there was no need since the doctor's malpractice insurance covered her. When Carol's employer was sued for failure to diagnose oral cancer, Carol was named as a co-defendant in the suit, as she had seen the patient for a preventive care appointment within the past year. While being named in any lawsuit was unsettling, Carol figured she really had nothing to worry about. She knew the doctor had malpractice insurance. What Carol did not know was that lawsuits can actually exceed the limits of the doctor's malpractice coverage. According to Jeff Tonner, JD, monetary awards for failure to diagnose oral cancer are the most common lawsuits to exceed the limits of coverage. If a lawsuit is successful and the limits of coverage are exceeded, co-defendants can be saddled with monetary damages, as the doctor is the primary defendant.

False Security

Jan chose not to carry malpractice insurance. She felt it was really a waste of money, since she knew her employer's malpractice insurance covered her.

One day, Jan accidentally sliced her patient's tongue when she slipped with a sharp instrument. The patient had to go to the hospital and get his tongue sutured. The patient subsequently sued the hygienist for damages. The doctor's malpractice insurance paid out a monetary settlement to the patient for damages. That should have been the end of the story, but unfortunately there was more to come. Since the doctor was not named in the suit, the insurance company sued the hygienist to recover what they had paid out on her behalf. The concept of "Respondeat Superior" is a Latin phrase that means let the master answer. It means that the owner/doctor of the practice is responsible for the acts of omission and commission of employees while engaging in delivery of dentistry. It is also called 'vicarious liability,' meaning that although the doctor may not have been involved in an injury to a patient (such as when a hygienist accidentally injures a patient), the doctor is still responsible. However, there is nothing to prevent a malpractice carrier from suing a staff member to recover the monetary amounts paid out on a staff member's behalf.

Surprise Surprise!

Mona had practiced dental hygiene in Texas for 15 years without malpractice insurance. One day, she accidentally spilled a chemical on her patient that caused a burn to the patient's lip. The patient had to see a plastic surgeon and endure pain and suffering associated with the accident. The patient was left with a scar, and she sued Mona.

What a surprise it was to Mona to find out her employer did not have any malpractice insurance! She did not realize that the state of Texas does not require doctors to carry malpractice insurance.

Policy Stipulations

It was a day like any other in the office where Mary had worked for one year. However, Mary would never forget this day. As her elderly patient stood up to exit the treatment room, he cut a gash in his scalp when he staggered and hit his head on the overhead light. He lashed out at Mary that it was her fault, that she should have pushed it out of the way. After a trip to the emergency room, the patient had nine stitches in his scalp.

After consulting an attorney, the patient decided to sue Mary. She had no malpractice insurance of her own, and the doctor's policy carried a stipulation that employees would only be covered if the dentist was named in the suit. The patient chose not to name the dentist. Some policies state that if both employer and dental hygienist are named in a suit and the employer's name is later dropped, the insurance policy may not cover the dental hygienist. In this case, Mary may have to countersue her employer's malpractice carrier or even her employer to get relief.

Types of Malpractice Coverage

It is true that hygienists are not sued nearly as often as dentists are sued, but the above examples point to the necessity of additional malpractice coverage for dental hygienists. The good news is that malpractice coverage is very reasonably priced for hygienists, typically less than $100/year for coverage.

There are two types of professional liability insurance. The first and most comprehensive coverage is called an *occurrence policy*. This type of policy protects the clinician for any alleged malpractice that occurs during the policy period. It does not matter when the claim is filed. With an occurrence policy, the clinician is afforded protection after leaving clinical practice even if the policy is not still in force at the time a claim is made. The coverage extends to the period after the clinician retires, so no additional coverage is needed.

The second (and most common) type of liability insurance is called *claims made policy*. The policy protects the clinician against claims made only while the policy is active and the clinician is actively engaged in clinical practice. If a clinician retires or leaves practice and a claim is filed after the policy is no longer in force, the clinician has no coverage. With this type of coverage, it may be prudent for the clinician to purchase an additional policy (called 'tail coverage') to protect for a limited period of time after leaving practice. For example, consider that a dental hygienist retires or leaves clinical practice in June. In July, a patient files a malpractice suit claiming the hygienist injured him or practiced in a negligent manner during an appointment one month before she left practice. If the hygienist had purchased a 'tail coverage' policy to extend her coverage for a time, she would be protected.

Before purchasing any type of policy, be sure that you understand any exclusions set forth (sometimes in small print) in the policy. Also, ask for availability of additional coverage should you be contemplating leaving practice.

Ten Areas of Potential Liability for Dental Hygienists

1. Failure to update medical history—High-quality chart records are the most important aspect of preventing a patient lawsuit from ever reaching the courts, and the medical history update is of primary importance. According to information provided to the ADA from malpractice carriers, failure to update the medical history is among the top five record-keeping errors. In fact, the medical history should be updated at **every** patient visit.

One thing every clinician should be clear about is that responsibility for completing the medical history does not rest entirely on the patient. Rather, it is the clinician's responsibility to obtain the medical history. So, when patients balk or express consternation about filling out their medical history, the clinician should take over the responsibility and go through the questions one on one. Consider that, according to the U.S. Department of Education National Adult Literacy Survey, almost half of the U.S. population is either functionally illiterate or only marginally literate.

2. Failure to detect oral cancer—Attorney Jeff Tonner posits that, in his experience, the failure to detect oral cancer is the primary reason hygienists are named as co-defendants when the doctor is sued for failure to diagnose. By virtue of their education, hygienists are trained to spot abnormalities in the oral cavity. Too many hygienists operate in the 'run and gun' mode and omit the most important aspect of the patient visit.

Common causes of liability for failure to diagnose or delayed diagnosis of oral cancer fall into four major categories: errors in clinical judgment, failure to follow-up, failure to screen patients appropriately, and evaluation delays. Screening for oral cancer should include a thorough history and physical examination of the head and neck region, including a visual inspection and palpation of the head, neck, oral and pharyngeal areas. It should also include a review of the social, familial, and medical history of the patient along with risk behaviors (tobacco and alcohol usage—people who drink and smoke are 15X more likely to have an oral cancer), a history of head and neck radiotherapy, familial history of head and neck cancer, and a personal history of cancer. All patients over 40 years of age should be considered at a higher risk for oral cancer than patient younger than age 40.

The bottom line is this: Any patient with a suspicious lesion should be kept under a "magnifying glass" until the clinician is certain of the diagnosis or the lesion resolves.

3. Failure to detect periodontal disease—Hygienists typically are in a co-diagnosis role in discovering periodontal disease through periodontal charting, tissue assessment and radiographs. It is incumbent upon the hygienist to perform timely periodontal assessments and keep radiographs current. The standard of care is one full-mouth probing with all numbers recorded once per year. Radiographs should be taken at an interval appropriate to the patient. *(See ADA document http://ada.org/ sections/scienceAndResearch/pdfs_topics_radiography_examinations.pdf)*

4. Injury to a patient—Unfortunately, accidents usually occur when we least expect them to happen. It is our responsibility to practice according to established standards that minimize the chance of an untoward event. It has been noted by some risk management experts that apologizing to a patient who has been injured is an important part of keeping the lines of communication open and preventing lawsuits.

5. *Failure to record thorough documentation in patient chart*—Records are the backbone of the clinician's defense in any malpractice claim. Make sure you record all the pertinent events in the appointment, including materials used and instructions given to the patient.

6. *Not protecting patient privacy/divulging confidential patient information*—Never, never discuss patient information outside the confines of the office, even with your spouse unless your spouse works in the practice.

7. *Failure to ask if patient has premedicated*—According to the newest premedication guidelines published in April 2007, many people who formerly required premedication are exempt from taking antibiotics before the dental visit. It is in the clinician's best interest to require that physicians prescribe antibiotics if they desire certain patients to premedicate prior to dental procedures. This prevents the dentist from being sued if the patient experiences an antibiotic reaction.

8. *Failure to inform about treatment options and consequences of non-treatment*—The hygienist must ensure that the patient understands the proposed treatment and the ramifications of non-treatment.

9. *Practicing outside the legal scope of practice*—Practice acts differ from state to state, so dental hygienists must be fully informed of the practice act in the state where she or he practices.

10. *Fraud*—Dental hygienists have a legal and moral responsibility to report their services truthfully. To do otherwise puts the hygienist as risk for lengthy court proceedings and possible jail time.

Where to Purchase Malpractice Insurance

Malpractice insurance may be purchased through Marsh at the following website: https://www.proliability.com/. Click on the dropdown box that says, "Select Your Profession," then click on "Dental Assistant/ Hygienist." Then you will be prompted to answer some questions. Another source is a company called Health Providers Service Organization, or HPSO, Inc. (hpso.com)

"Informed Consent"

Dear Dianne,

I am a dental hygienist working in a public health clinic. We see many minors with urgent dental needs. We know we are supposed to have a signed consent for any patient who is a minor. However, recently we had a pregnant 16 year old who does not live at home. She had a large carious lesion on a molar. We were not able to get a signed consent for her, as she is estranged from her parents. The patient became very angry when the doctor opted not to treat her without consent. She told us she was emancipated, but she did not have any written verification of that status. She even threatened to sue us and stated rather vehemently that she did not need parental consent. Did we do the right thing? Somehow, it does not feel right to turn someone away with urgent needs simply because we could not get a parental signature. Also, what about parents who drop their children off for treatment and leave the premises to do errands? Is there a law that requires parents to stay on the premises while their child is being treated?

Concerned in Maryland

Dear Concerned,

Your inquiry prompted me to do some research. According to an article on treating minors, a minor who is married, pregnant, or the parent of a child has the same capacity as an adult to consent to medical/dental treatment (http://irb.jhmi.edu/Guidelines/Informed_Consent_Minors).

Being pregnant means she can give her own consent and does not require the consent of a parent. Therefore, the patient in question was correct in that she did not need outside consent. (This law may vary in other states.)

Informed consent for minors is about a parent's or guardian's understanding and willingness to voluntarily agree to proposed treatment after the recommended treatment, alternate treatment options, and the benefits and risks of treatment have been thoroughly described to the parent in common language. Informed consent must be voluntary. Informed consent originates from the legal right the patient has to direct what happens to his or her body and from the ethical duty of the healthcare provider to involve that patient in his or her own healthcare. According to Burton Pollack, DDS, JD, many instances of malpractice involve the failure to obtain a valid consent for treatment. Lack of consent can be treated by the courts as assault and battery or negligence.

Some general facts about consent are:

- It must be informed and freely given.

- In the case of an emergency, consent can be implied by law.

- Telephone consent is permissible if it contains all the elements of a valid consent, i.e., the parent/guardian be contacted and a third party be listening on an extension.

- It can be obtained by the doctor or an agent of the doctor, such as an auxiliary staff member.

- Written consent is required for some procedures, particularly surgical procedures or those with significant risks. However, consent need not be in writing to be valid.

- Consent may be implied by the actions of the patient when (1) the patient was aware of the need for treatment, and (2) the patient made no objection when treatment began.

- The patient must have opportunity to ask questions.

In dealing with parents and minors who are patients of record, there is not a huge likelihood that a clinician would be charged criminally if something happened, such as the child having a seizure or an allergic reaction. According to Casey Crafton, DDS, JD, of Columbia, Maryland, the act of mom dropping a child off for treatment could be taken as 'implied' permission. However, there is always the possibility that something untoward or unforeseen could happen.

Petra von Heimburg, DDS, JD, of Barrington, Illinois (www.ceprofseminars.com), offers this perspective:

"Every office should think long and hard about their policies regarding the treatment of minors. This is an area of the 'judgment call.' For example, I would not suggest that an office allow a parent to drop off a 5 year old and leave the facility. I would also suggest that when the minor (of any age) is undergoing oral surgery that the parent/legal guardian is present. An office should tailor their treatment policy regarding minors to its 'comfort level.'

From a practical perspective, some offices may feel comfortable being more "liberal" in their policies. Here is a sample letter that could be used:

Dear Parent,

It is the office policy that the parent/legal guardian may leave the facility while the minor is being treated, provided that:

a. the minor is over the age of 10 years OR

b. the procedure to be done involves routine dental treatment, such as cleaning, fluoride treatment, or fillings AND

c. the parent/legal guardian is available by phone AND

d. the parent/legal guardian has signed all the required documentation AND

e. the parent/legal guardian has informed the office beforehand that he/she will be leaving the facility or that he/she will not be present.

We will inform the parent/legal guardian at what time the treatment is expected to be completed. In case the minor is being picked up, we expect the parent/legal guardian to return on time. (See Appendix B for a sample Informed Consent)

Finally, the safest course of action is to have a signed consent and ask parents of young children to remain on the premises while dentistry is being provided. Good patient relationships and open communication lessen the possibility of litigation.

Best wishes,

Dianne

"Fraudulent Credentials"

Dear Dianne,

I work with a dental assistant who earned her Certified Dental Assistant (CDA) certification a few years ago but has failed to renew as she should. It seems wrong to me that she wears the professional designation on her name tag when she has not maintained her credentials. It has crossed my mind to report her, but I don't know if I should or not. What do you think? Should I report her?

Irked Coworker

Dear Irked,

As you know, certification and licensure are two different things. People who are licensed to do a particular job cannot legally perform that job without the license. In order to maintain licensure, hygienists and dentists are required pay a yearly renewal fee and, in some states, to obtain a designated number of continuing education credits and current CPR certification.

A certification in dental assisting means the assistant has successfully passed an examination administered by the Dental Assisting National Board. In many cases, the certification is not legally required for a dental assistant to perform basic assisting duties. It is, however, recognized by many states as one way to meet basic and/or expanded duties requirements for dental assistants in that state. In addition, the CDA or other DANB credentials may be used in lieu of licensure in some states. If the dental assistant is using the CDA to meet the state requirements, and then does not maintain that credential, she or he must contact the state dental board to see if it requires him or her to then provide proof of meeting the alternate pathway to eligibility to perform those functions in that state.

States vary on the allowable duties for assistants, but advanced training is required for many expanded functions for assistants, such as coronal polishing and exposing radiographs. To see what is required for dental assistants in your state, go to www.danb.org and click on State-Specific Information.

I contacted a representative of DANB to get more information. I learned that the CDA examination costs from $300-$340, depending on the format. There is a $55 yearly renewal fee (and an additional $10 late fee for renewals past a three-month grace period). CDAs must show proof of obtaining 12 continuing education units per year and a front-and-back copy of their current CPR card. It is interesting that DANB requires more continuing education units for assistants than some states require for hygienists. One example is North Carolina, which requires only six continuing education units per year for hygienists.

If a CDA allows the certification to lapse beyond the three-month grace period, there is a $125 fee for re-instatement plus the missed renewal fee of $65, totaling $190. The assistant receives a letter that confirms the lapse and instructs the individual to discontinue using the 'CDA' certification mark.

According to Cynthia Durley, MEd, MBA, Executive Director of DANB, Inc., it is a serious matter when someone fraudulently uses the CDA certification mark, which can result in legal action. The individual "may be subject to disciplinary action, including but not limited to temporary or permanent denial or revocation of eligibility, certification, or recertification. Any individual who engages in such irregular behavior also may be subject to legal action." Ms. Durley stated that the state board of dentistry would be notified and the employer/dentist would be warned that the employee is in violation of DANB's Code of Professional Conduct and DANB's Disciplinary Policy and in danger of disciplinary action.

I have always felt that professional designations are important, just as being a member of one's professional association is important. Yet, I know plenty of hygienists who are not members of ADHA. The excuse they usually give is that it costs too much. Your coworker may feel the same about the renewal fees and continuing education requirements to maintain her CDA certification. However, the CDA is not a membership designation, but a professional certification and a Registered Trademark, recognized or required by 37 states, which denotes that one has met or exceeded minimum dental assisting competency standards. It is ethically and morally wrong for the assistant to continue to use the 'CDA' designation without following the rules set forth by DANB. In addition, misusing the certification mark violates national trademark law.

If the assistant is a good and competent assistant, the doctor may not care if she has a professional certification or not. However, if the doctor is allowing the assistant to perform duties in a state that requires her to hold the CDA credential, then he is also in danger of facing disciplinary action by the state dental board. The doctor should care about her enough to make paying her renewal fee and continuing education credits part of her benefits package because patients will respect her credentials. He should also care enough about his employees and patients to make sure that only those qualified to hold credentials or perform certain functions are allowed to do so. Employing highly skilled and ethical, honest employees is a reflection of the doctor's values toward patient care.

Please consider the consequences of reporting your coworker to DANB. If you report her and she finds it out, there will always be a chasm between you. She will feel like you betrayed her. If you report her anonymously, she will probably figure it was someone in her office, most likely a coworker. How would you answer her if she asked you directly if you reported her? Would you be willing to tell her the truth, or would you deny what you did? If you hide behind a lie, then you would be guilty of the same offense as your coworker.

However, if you are a CDA or have passed any other DANB national exams and fail to report her, you are jeopardizing your own credential, because you will be acting outside of DANB's Code of Professional Conduct. In addition, you are diminishing the value of your own CDA by looking the other way when people use it who have not met the qualifications to do so.

In this particular situation, I would probably inquire about the certification with her directly, "Hey Carol, how many CEUs have you earned this year? Don't you have to have 12 units to keep your certification? Can you legally use the CDA designation if you do not comply with their rules? You know, this could be construed as an ethics violation of state law." She knows everyone knows that she is using the CDA credential fraudulently. If her conscience does not bother her enough to do something about it, she has an even bigger problem than violating the CDA ethics and perhaps breaking the law. Your discreet and gentle urging may be enough to persuade her to come into compliance.

I urge you to weigh all the facts concerning this situation and speak with the doctor privately about the matter. He may be able to help this staff member get back into compliance right away. Certainly, that would be the best scenario for all involved.

Best wishes,

Dianne

Trisha O'Hehir and Linda Jorgenson.

The Consummate Dental Hygienist

"Uncompensated Hours"

Dear Dianne,

I have been working in dental hygiene over 20 years, always receiving a flat daily rate of pay. Presently, I work three days per week. About six months ago, my boss made the decision to put me on commission. When he presented this to me, I had no part in the decision. He had obviously done the math and showed me what I could expect to make. I knew other hygienists who worked on commission, and they seemed to like the arrangement. So, I thought it might be a good thing. The doctor told me that if I did not have a patient, I was free to do whatever I wanted, which included going home or running errands. Today, the doctor called me into his office and told me that he now expects me to work on recall at least 3 hours/week, all for NO pay. He said if my schedule is not full, then I should come in on my day off and work on recall. He said if I refuse, I will lose my job. I was speechless!

My question to you is this: Is this legal? Can he force me to work like this? I don't know where to turn to find the right answers.

Sheryl in N.C.

Dear Sheryl,

On the surface, it sounds like your boss is stressing out over paying you when you don't have a patient in your chair. I would assume there have been some problems with downtime in the hygiene schedule. If this is the case, it needs to be addressed, but that is a separate issue.

I have heard of doctors requiring staff members to attend staff meetings or courses uncompensated. I have also heard of doctors who require work pertaining to the practice to be done at home or on non-patient days, again with no expectation of compensation.

To require an employee to report to work and expect no compensation for 'X' number of hours worked is blatantly illegal. I went to the website for the Fair Labor Standards Act and found this information.

The amount of pay due an employee cannot be determined without knowing the total number of hours actually worked by that employee in each workweek. An employee must be paid for all of the time considered to be hours worked and all time that is hours worked must be counted when determining overtime hours worked.

If you are required to be at the office performing a duty, that is compensable time, period.

Here is a partial list of compensable duties:

- Coffee and snack breaks

- Fire drills

- Grievance adjustment during time employee is required to be on premises

- Meal periods if employees are not relieved of duties, if not free to leave posts or if too short to be useful (less than 30 minutes)

- Medical attention on plant premises or if employer directs outside treatment

- Meetings to discuss daily operations problems

- Rest periods of 20 minutes or less

- Retail sales product meetings sponsored by employer

- Show-up time if employees are required to remain on premises before being sent home

- Stand-by time—remaining at post during lunch period or temporary shut down

- Suggestion systems

- Travel from preliminary instructional meeting to work site

- Waiting while on duty

There is also another category that includes time spent before, after, or between regular work hours that is compensable. It includes the following:

- Arranging or putting merchandise away

- Changing clothes, showering or washing if required by the nature of the work (such as job with chemicals requires bathing for worker health)

- Civic or charitable work if requested by employer or controlled by employer or if required to be performed on employer's premises

- Clearing cash register or totaling receipts

- Discussing work problems at shift change

- Distributing work to work benches

- Equipment maintenance before or after shift

- Homework under contract with employer

- Make-ready work, preparatory work necessary for principal activity

- On-call time if employee must stay on or near premises so as to have liberty restricted or not use time as the employee pleases

- Physical exam required for continued service

From this information, you can see that any time spent in the office performing any number of office tasks is compensable. Also, time spent getting ready for work, stocking, etc., are compensable as well. These laws and standards were developed to prevent employers from taking advantage of their employees by requiring them to work uncompensated.

It is also very important that employers keep accurate records on their employees. FLSA requires no particular form for the records, but does require that the records include certain identifying information about the employee and data about the hours worked and the wages earned. The law requires this information to be accurate. The following is a listing of the basic records that an employer must maintain:

- Employee's full name and Social Security number

- Address, including zip code

- Birth date, if younger than 19

- Sex and occupation

- Time and day of week when employee's workweek begins

- Hours worked each day

- Total hours worked each workweek

- Basis on which employee's wages are paid (e.g., "$6 an hour", "$220 a week", "piecework")
- Regular hourly pay rate
- Total daily or weekly straight-time earnings
- Total overtime earnings for the workweek
- All additions to or deductions from the employee's wages
- Total wages paid each pay period
- Date of payment and the pay period covered by the payment

Working on a commission basis is considered 'piecework' compensation under the law. If the doctor requires you to perform non-clinical duties such as calling patients to schedule appointments, he must pay you a mutually agreed-upon rate for that time. Since you have been working on a commission basis for six months, you could find your true hourly rate by dividing the number of hours you work into the gross amount. However, the doctor is not required to pay you that same rate for office work versus what you make while seeing patients. The concept is called "different capacity work rate." The same thing applies when being compensated for attending staff meetings or continuing education meetings.

The doctor would do well to consider how he would feel if he was an employee and was required to work 'x' number of hours/week for no compensation or a significantly smaller amount of money than he normally made. No doubt, he would be resentful of such an arrangement, as would anybody. Further, how can anyone be motivated to do their best work when that person feels the work is unreasonable and unfair? This is a no-win situation.

I have never felt it is a good use of a hygienist's time performing front office duties. That is not to say that hygienists should not help out at the front (or anywhere in the office) during downtime. Hygienists working on a daily or hourly rate should be available to help anywhere they are needed when they are not actually at chairside with patients. Commissioned hygienists are under no obligation to do anything but chairside hygiene and duties that are directly associated. However, there are many commissioned hygienists who help other staff members when the opportunity arises, simply because they are team oriented.

Scheduling and maintaining the hygiene schedule is a front office function that needs to be a part of a business assistant's job description. Hygienists are typically the highest paid staff members, and rightly so, because they are producers. In most situations, hygienists will produce far more than they actually make in wages. Your situation is unfortunate, because it appears you have been singled out and burdened with unreasonable demands because of your high rate of pay. If the problem is a less-than-full schedule, attention needs to be placed at the source of the problem, which is scheduling protocol and maintenance. If, after discussing the particular legalities of what you are being asked to do, your employer persists with his mandate, you may call **1-866-4-USA-DOL** Monday-Friday from 8-5 and seek further assistance with this matter.

Best Wishes,

Dianne

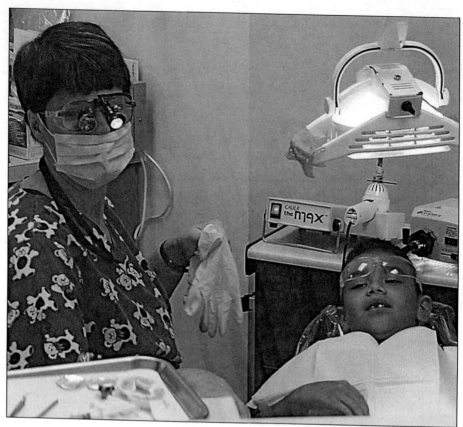

Shirley Cross, RDH.

The Consummate Dental Hygienist

"Wrongful Termination"

Dear Dianne,

Recently, I had an 85-year-old man on my schedule who was in poor health. He was formerly indicated for antibiotic premedication for a knee replacement. The patient stated that he had forgotten to take his premedication. He first said he would reschedule, but the doctor I work with interjected that he did not think my patient needed any premedication. Knowing how the patient had been prone to bleeding because of his periodontal condition, I stated that maybe it would be prudent to call the patient's physician. The doctor stated rather firmly that no such call was necessary and for me to proceed as scheduled.

The patient asked me about consequences of not premedicating, and I told him that he could become very ill. The patient then asked me to just do a "light cleaning." I recommended he take his premedication and call his doctor when he got home, and I noted the conversation in the patient chart.

When the doctor read my chart notes, he came into my room and yelled at me in front of my coworkers and other patients in the office. He asked me to give him one good reason why he should not fire me. He asked me why I did not follow the new guidelines, and I said I felt I was. My patient's health was compromised. The doctor was upset I did not do a 'periodontal prophy' and became very abusive and hostile. Naturally, I became very upset and requested to talk with him in private. He said he wanted me to finish the afternoon, and we would talk after work.

The rest of the day he was very rude to me. After work when I went into his office to talk to him, rather than discuss the issue rationally, he led me out of his office and fired me in front of all my coworkers. He said I embarrassed him in front of the patient and that I was insubordinate and practicing beyond the scope of my license.

I was speechless! I have worked in this office full time for seven years and have never had any confrontations with the doctor. His anger and subsequent firing cut me to the bone!

My actions in wanting to notify the patient's physician were based on my concern that, due to the patient's compromised health situation, the physician may feel premedication was prudent. I did not feel I was out of line, nor did I have any intention of overstepping my boundaries. I was simply concerned about my patient.

To make matters worse, it has now been over six months, and I have not been able to find a full-time position due to the overabundance of hygienists in my area.

My question to you is this: Was this firing justified? Should I have just blindly accepted what the doctor said, even though my own professional judgment felt compromised?

Still Hurting in California

Dear Still Hurting,

What a sad state of affairs! I can only imagine how difficult these months have been since your termination.

By a "light cleaning," I'm assuming he meant for you to tip-toe around the sulcus to avoid bleeding, right? What would that accomplish? Exactly nothing, as there is no therapeutic advantage to supragingival scaling and polishing for a patient with periodontal disease. The patient wasted his money.

There is a variety of state and federal laws that protect employees from wrongful termination. There are several categories of wrongful termination, such as discrimination, defamation of character, breach of contract, constructive discharge, retaliation, and breach of good faith and fair dealing. It is the last two categories that I feel are pertinent to your situation.

First, termination for retaliatory reasons can be considered wrongful termination under certain conditions. Employers cannot rightfully terminate employees for reporting their illegal actions to the proper authorities, commonly known as whistle blowing. They also cannot fire employees in retaliation for something they legally or illegally did, or because someone refused to do something that was contrary to public policy and sound morality, such as breaking the law. According to Niznick (2007), "values, principles, and basic rules that the courts and legislatures consider to be in the best interest of individuals and the general public" are considered public policy. Public policy may be written or implied and can vary among states. Given the fact that the patient was elderly, had compromised health in general, and had formerly been indicated for pre-medication, interfacing with the patient's physician seems prudent and in the patient's best interest. The dentist's expressed concern that you embarrassed him adds fuel to his actions being retaliatory.

Additionally, some states recognize the covenant of good faith and fair dealing. What this means is that employers have the burden to deal with employees, especially dedicated, long-term employees, with fairness and good faith. Your employer seems to have violated this principle, not only with the termination itself but also the way he terminated you in front of your coworkers. The only positive note here is that all your coworkers were witnesses to his rudeness.

Does your former employer have an office manual that describes a graduated discipline or termination process? If so, he may have violated his own policy, which also could be deemed wrongful termination.

Most employers hire employees "at-will," meaning that both the employer and employee may terminate the employment relationship at any time. However, employers cannot legally terminate employees for illegal reasons.

Depending upon the situation, damages available to wrongfully discharged employees can include back pay, promotion, reinstatement, front pay, compensatory damages, required reasonable accommodations, injunctive relief, punitive damages, and attorneys' fees.

Hygienists are taught to be diligent about all aspects of patient care, including contacting a patient's physician regarding medical issues that may influence the course of treatment. In my opinion, your concern was warranted in this case and, in most offices, it would have been the standard of care to contact the patient's physician to ask about the necessity for premedication. Calling the physician would have been a simple step to alleviate concerns in everyone's mind and would have shown the patient that the practice considers patient safety a number one priority. The doctor's mandate to proceed with scheduled treatment without contacting the physician could possibly erode the patient's confidence in the doctor. Patients are not stupid. It is possible the physician would have said, "No, this patient does not need premedication," and everyone would have been relieved.

If the doctor had acted rationally by talking with you in private about the situation, it is possible everything could have been settled amicably. However, it would appear he felt he needed to make an example of you by treating you in such a harsh manner. When it comes to patient care, there is no room for egos.

Considering your months of lost pay and earning potential, my advice would be to find an attorney who is willing to take your case on a contingency basis. There is no guarantee of victory, but given that you did nothing deserving of firing, you may be able to put closure on this unfortunate chapter of your life through the legal system.

Best Wishes,

Dianne

References:
Niznick, J. (2007) Public policy. Retrieved November 5, 2007 from http://jobsearchtech.about.com/od/careereducation/g/public_policy.htm
"Wrongful Termination." (2007) Retrieved November 5, 2007 from http://jobsearchtech.about.com/od/laborlaws/l/aa102300_2.htm
"Ten Things to Think About: Wrongful Discharge." (2007) Retrieved November 5, 2007 from http://employment.findlaw.com/employment/employment-employee-job-loss/le9_2ten.html

"Records Adulteration"

Dear Dianne,

A few months ago, the doctor saw a regular patient for a toothache. He wondered why I had missed this "huge hole" on #13, as I have seen the patient for cleanings regularly. I was dumbfounded. I have proven to him to be meticulous with finding even the smallest areas of decay, and if the doctor is not in the office when I see patients, patients are always scheduled for yearly exams. I didn't understand what happened. The patient ended up getting a root canal and crown.

About three weeks ago, the patient came in for her regular cleaning. When I opened the chart, all my notes from the past two years were no longer there. They had been replaced with notes the office manager had written and then forged my name and title behind them! I took a deep breath and continued with my patient like nothing was wrong. She happened to be my last patient of the day. Neither the doctor nor the office manager was in the office that day, so I called and spoke with the doctor, who was home on medical leave. He said when he returned, the three of us would discuss this. So far, nothing has been discussed.

Here's what I believe happened. The doctor or office manager was not in the office when I saw the patient, and the patient was asked to return for an exam. The office manager failed to contact the patient and have her return for the exam. I believe the reason she re-wrote everything is because I noted the decay and that the patient needed to return. Our office protocol is that the office manager is supposed to call the patient and schedule her. Obviously, she failed to follow up.

I called the state board. The contact there said since the office manager is not a licensed professional, they cannot take action against her. They recommended I speak with the doctor and try to resolve the issue or file a complaint against him.

Today, I spoke with a local attorney who acted like this was no big deal and looked at me like I was a little crazy. Basically, he said I should not go after the doctor, as it will make it very difficult for me to ever get a job again. He said that I need to request that the doctor provide me with a positive letter of recommendation and not retaliate against me for seeking new employment. Quite honestly, it's not the doctor I am worried about.
It is his wife. She has a long history of retaliation and making the working

environment unpleasant. Unfortunately, finding a new job has proven to be very difficult in these times. I truly feel as if I am stuck in this office for the time being, and I am afraid of making matters worse for myself by continuing to ask the doctor to address this issue with his wife. What should I do?

California RDH

Dear California,

This is one of the most egregious acts of records adulteration I have ever encountered! It is a serious legal issue. When I taught in a hygiene school, records adulteration was one infraction that could cause a student to be dismissed from the program.

Records adulteration is one of the major reasons that dentists lose malpractice cases. I know of an oral surgeon, who, when he found out he was being sued, tried to add to his chart notes. The courts used ink-dating technology to prove the notes were not contemporaneous. His credibility was destroyed, and he lost the case.

In your case, the courts would have no trouble proving the forged signature is not your own. Current record evaluation methods include ink analysis, light reflection tests, transmission analysis, and computerized handwriting analysis. I expect you would have an open-and-shut case for forgery against the office manager.

Do you think the wife did this with her husband's blessing? It seems obvious that she is ignorant of the serious potential consequences of her actions. In trying to cover their negligence, she made the situation far worse. She has committed two illegal acts—records adulteration and forgery.

What to do. Let's consider your options. If you file a complaint against the doctor with the dental board, you create an atmosphere of hostility and your job is toast. I expect you would not want to be there. While retaliatory firing is illegal, consider the negative workplace atmosphere that would result. The doctor is ultimately responsible for the acts of omission and commission of employees. Undoubtedly, the dental board would take the office manager's actions very seriously. Any punitive action by the dental board would have long-lasting consequences for the doctor. There would be an investigation, the patient would have to be examined by an outside consultant, and the patient would have full knowledge of the situation. While it is clear the record was altered, it would be your word against the doctor's word. They might try to make up some excuse as to why the record was re-written, like, "I spilled coffee on it and ruined it," or some such garbage.

You could file a lawsuit against the office manager over the forgery. Are you prepared for legal fees and the hassle of a lawsuit? I expect this could only make matters worse.

Everybody makes mistakes, and with all that goes on at the front desk, it would have been easy to forget to call the patient to come back for a timely examination. The patient was not irreparably damaged, although she did have to endure endo and crown procedures. Even with a timely exam, the patient may have still needed those procedures. Sometimes the decay is much deeper than it appears on the X-ray, and I expect with the time frame of just a few weeks/months between her prophy and the toothache, the decay was probably either dangerously near or already into the pulp.

Consider the consequences of forcing dialog about the situation with the doctor. Your knowledge of records adulteration and forgery puts you in a position of power, and he may feel threatened by you. The concept of 'respondeat superior' is a Latin phrase that means literally "Let the master answer." So although it was his wife who committed the illegal acts, he is ultimately responsible. Again, this has the potential of creating a hostile work environment. Everybody has a "self-preservation" mode.

Please don't misunderstand, though. Nothing—and I do mean nothing—excuses the wife's forgery of your name and records adulteration. You have every right to feel angry, disrespected, and threatened. I have no doubt that the doctor would feel the same negative emotions if someone forged his name to chart notes he did not write.

I think it goes without saying that you do need to leave that practice as soon as you can secure other employment. You may feel stuck at the moment, but if you are like most people, you need to pay your bills and survive.

Be sure you have carefully documented those conversations and dates with the state board and the attorney, just in case this thing bubbles to the surface again. The only negative thing I can think of would be if the patient would decide to sue the doctor for malpractice at a later date. He could decide to try to implicate you, but again, he is ultimately responsible. You can prove through handwriting experts that the notes are not your own handwriting.

You have to weigh all the options. Sometimes, taking definitive action makes things worse. My own self-preservation trumps any satisfaction I may receive from bringing someone down, especially if such actions hurt me and my family.

Best wishes,

Dianne

"Patients Who Refuse X-rays"

Dear Dianne,

One of the problems I have been experiencing more and more is with patients who refuse to allow me to take X-rays. The doctor wants us to get new bite-wings on every patient once per year, but some patients just won't allow it.

How should I handle these rejections?

Delaware Hygienist

Dear Delaware,

First off, we need to establish that radiographs are a necessary part of good patient care. Since we can see only about one third of the actual tooth, radiographs provide valuable information about aspects of the tooth that we cannot visualize otherwise.

I remember a patient who consistently refused to allow X-rays. On a particular preventive visit, the doctor asked to see her radiographs. When I told him that Mrs. XXX requested that none be taken, he looked at her and said, "Really? What's that about?" While the patient was responding, he reached in his back pocket, took out a handkerchief, and began tying it around his eyes like a blindfold. He then reached out and said, "Dianne, hand me the mirror," as if he was going to do the exam blindfolded! The patient started laughing, but she got the point when he told her that treating her without radiographs was like asking him to work with a blindfold. Then she said, "OK, OK, I get the point," and I took her films. The point is that it is our duty to provide competent care, and radiographs are vital to proper diagnoses. Without the necessary films, we compromise our ability to provide competent care.

However, you stated that the rule in your office is "bitewings on every patient once/year." I take issue with the wisdom of such a mandate. Some patients are caries free and have been their whole lives. Certainly, patients like this do not need radiographs as often as patients who have had moderate or high caries experience. Further, patients with healthy periodontium do not need radiographs as often as patients with a history of periodontitis. In some cases, there are extenuating circumstances that make exposing radiographs prudent, such as implants, endodontics, and pathology.

published "Guidelines for Prescribing Dental Radiographs" (ada.org). Here is a sample of those recommendations:

...ent with no clinical caries and not at increased risk for caries:

■ Child with primary or transitional dentition
Posterior bitewing exam at 12-24 month intervals if proximal surfaces cannot be examined visually or with a probe

■ Adolescent with permanent dentition
Posterior bitewing exam at 18-36 month intervals

■ Adult dentate or partially edentulous
Posterior bitewing exam at 24-36 month intervals

■ Recall patient* with periodontal disease:
Clinical judgment as to the need for and type of radiographic images

■ Patient with other circumstances including, but not limited to, proposed or existing implants, pathology, restorative/endodontic needs, treated periodontal disease and caries remineralization:
Clinical judgment as to the need for and type of radiographic images

The bottom line is that we should use sound judgment and common sense in deciding when patients need X-rays and not abide by some arbitrary standard that says everyone gets them every year or six-month recare interval. Too many times, we allow insurance companies to determine when we expose radiographs. Further, we should not expose radiographs just because the patient's insurance allows it. We need to have a valid reason for taking radiographs that is dictated by our patients' needs. The average time interval in most offices is 18–24 months, but can vary depending on the needs of the patient. The full ADA document can be accessed at: http://www.ada.org/sections/scienceAndResearch/pdfs/topics_radiography_examinations.pdf

As an example, let's say Joe Blow comes in today for his preventive appointment. His last bitewings were taken three years ago, and he requested no radiographs on his last visit which was seven months ago. He chews tobacco and has had several carious lesions in the past. Knowing his history of refusing radiographs, a hygienist might feel intimidated even broaching the subject. I can hear the hygienist voicing the need for radiographs: "Mr. Blow, it has been three years since we took any X-rays on you. Is it OK if we get some today?" Joe, noticing the timidity with which the hygienist asks, boldly proclaims, "Nope, no X-rays!"

The problem is poor communication. Instead of asking his permission to do her job, she should have said, "Mr. Blow, **as the doctor has requested,** I'm going to take some necessary X-rays today." For all Joe knows, the doctor personally examined Joe's chart before he came in and instructed the hygienist to take X-rays. If Joe protests, the hygienist would say, "There has been a history of cavities in the past and tobacco chewing places you at a higher risk than non-users. The films are necessary to help us diagnose problems that we can't actually see with our eyes. Would you share with me why you do not want diagnostic X-rays?"

The usual concerns expressed by patients are (1) fear of radiation, (2) cost, and (3) discomfort. A few patients just have an unvarnished obstinance toward anything we want to do. Whatever the reason is, you should be equipped to address the concern.

Fear of radiation

Although X-ray machines vary, the amount of actual radiation exposure is anywhere from .1 to .5 of a second for one periapical exposure—an extremely small amount. Digital radiography is even lower than that.

I heard a doctor tell a patient once that people get more radiation exposure from their color televisions than from dental X-rays. Although this is an analogy a patient can understand, the accuracy of that statement is questionable. The point the doctor was trying to make was that we receive radiation from many different environmental sources, not just dental X-rays.

"Mrs. Jones, the truth is that dental X-rays are quite safe. The amount of radiation is extremely small due to the fast film speed (or digital technology) we use. These pictures provide us with valuable information about things we can't see under the gums, under fillings, and in between your teeth."

Cost

If the patient relates to you that s/he cannot afford to have X-rays taken, you have two choices:

(1) Offer to take complimentary films, or

(2) Make an agreement with the patient that the X-rays will be taken on the next recare visit so the patient can come prepared to pay for them.

Be sure to document thoroughly any conversation regarding future X-rays in the patient chart. There are probably instances when the real cause for objection of X-rays is fear, but the patient just uses finances as an excuse.

Discomfort

Some patients genuinely disdain X-rays because of discomfort. Tori (large or small), a strong gag reflex, or a small mouth with a shallow floor—these are all factors we must deal with in taking intraoral radiographs. Each case calls for special efforts from us to make the experience easier. Here are a few tips I have learned over the years:

(1) Tori—bend the film slightly to accommodate placement around bony protrusions. Also, use soft film edge-protectors that decrease discomfort.

(2) Gagging—use topical anesthetic to anesthetize the floor of the mouth and palatal areas. Another trick is to smear a small amount of salt on the sides of the tongue to help to quell the gag reflex. Some clinicians report that having the patient rinse with a mouthwash, such as Scope or Listerine, can eliminate gagging long enough to expose radiographs.

(3) Small mouth—use smaller size film or even pedo size.

(4) When all else fails, a panoramic film is better than no film at all.

(5) Although the use of rigid film holders increases the likelihood of a quality film, film holders are contraindicated for patients with any of the previously mentioned problems.

It is easy to understand why some patients dread having X-rays taken. We should do everything possible to carry out the X-ray procedure with a minimum of discomfort.

Legal Risks

Many offices have a policy that states if a patient refuses to have the necessary radiographs taken, that patient will be dismissed from the practice. While this practice may seem rather inflexible and even harsh, from a legal standpoint it may be the wisest policy. It should be understood that even if you have a patient sign a form stating s/he willingly refuses X-rays, no patient can give consent for the dentist to be negligent. If a radiograph is not taken when it is needed for proper diagnosis and a serious dental problem arises later on, the doctor could become entangled in a legal mess.

Patients have the choice of whether or not to proceed with recommended treatment. Patients can refuse any diagnostic test or treatment, including resuscitation, cancer treatment, or dental X-rays. However, doctors cannot provide care for patients based on an incomplete diagnosis without becoming subject to liability for failure to diagnose or treat existing conditions. This is a serious matter for the doctor. Good documentation in the patient record is an absolute necessity.

When the doctor decides that a patient should be dismissed from the practice for refusing radiographs, it is recommended by some risk management courses that the dismissal letter contain the phrase that failure to treat could result in **"permanent irreversible damage to your dental health."**

It is important for the doctor to get involved in discussions with patients about radiographs. The doctor may say this: "I understand your concerns about X-rays. But please understand my position that I cannot give you the care you deserve without radiographs. Please be prepared on your next visit for some X-rays." If, on the next visit, the patient again refuses, then the doctor may decide to dismiss the patient from the practice.

When patients understand how taking radiographs will result in some benefit directly to them, there is less likelihood for an objection. The bottom line is that we should use sound judgment and common sense in deciding when patients need X-rays and not abide by some arbitrary standard that says everyone gets them every year or six-month recare interval.

For the regular recare patient:

"Mrs. Jones, in order to check the areas I cannot see in between your teeth and under fillings, I am going to take some necessary X-rays."

For those procedures that you feel are necessary, it is best *not* to ask the patient's permission. Do not say, "Mrs. Jones, I'd like to update your X-rays today. Will that be OK?" Questions like this show hesitancy on the part of the clinician and make it easy for the patient to refuse.

*"Mrs. Jones, **as the doctor has requested,** I'm going to take some necessary X-rays. Let's do that first so the pictures will be ready when the doctor comes in."*

For the periodontal recare patient:

"Mrs. Jones, in order to check the bone around your teeth and to make sure things are remaining stable, I am going to take some necessary X-rays."

For the new patient who needs a full mouth series:

"Mrs. Jones, in order for us to properly treat you, some X-rays are needed. These pictures provide us with valuable information and help us see things we cannot see otherwise."

Script for person who refuses diagnostically necessary radiographs:

1. Patient states s/he cannot afford them.

"Mrs. Jones, I understand your concerns. Without an X-ray, I cannot make a clear diagnosis, so we will forego the fee today for the service."

2. Patient is unreasonably resistant. Ask the patient to share why s/he does not want radiographs. The **doctor** should take over the discussion at this point and proceed with this verbiage:

*"I understand your concerns. However, the state of_____ mandates that I treat you in a competent manner, and **I cannot do that without the necessary radiographs**. Please be prepared on your next visit for radiographs."*

On the subsequent visit, if the patient still resists, use this verbiage:

"The state of_____mandates that I treat you in a competent manner, and I cannot do that without the necessary X-rays. Therefore, I will be unable to continue to provide your care. I will be available to you for the next 30 days if you have a dental emergency."

If the doctor does not desire to have this conversation face to face with the patient, a similarly worded letter sent by certified mail will suffice.

Liability and Malpractice Risk

Doctors assume a legal risk if they retain patients who refuse needed radiographs. Even having a patient sign a form that states he/she declines X-rays will not protect a doctor should something untoward happen, such as a brain abscess that originates from an undiagnosed tooth abscess, or a bone cancer that was undiagnosed because of failure to obtain radiographs. There are documented cases of successful lawsuits from patients who had formerly refused needed radiographs when dental conditions go undiagnosed. The refusal of needed radiographs impedes the doctor's ability to diagnose. "Failure to diagnose" cases are usually won by complainants.

All licensed dental professionals are expected to perform their work according to certain standards of care. Licensure conveys a duty to provide competent care. Failure to do so, including maintaining current radiographs based on the patient's needs, increases the licensee's risk of malpractice.

Best wishes,

Dianne

The author and Linda Miles, CMC, CSP

Chapter 7

The Consummate Dental Hygienist

Consummate means the best of the best. All dental hygienists should aspire to be the best they can be. It is a journey! Knowing that the best always want to be better, there are two areas in which the hygienist must be a continual learner. First, there is the development of excellent clinical skill. Second, but just as important, is the development of excellent communication skill. The consummate dental hygienist is dedicated to taking high-quality continuing education classes that will help him/her continually upgrade those necessary skills. Here are 10 tips for becoming the consummate dental hygienist.

1. Know the numbers for the hygiene department.

Some offices will furnish you with a document, called a monitor, to assist you in tracking certain aspects of your daily practice, such as production, broken appointments, X-rays taken, adult prophys, etc. Other offices have excellent practice management software that will track things for you. Tracking shows that you are interested in knowing how productive you are and what you are contributing to the success of the practice.

2. Be a problem solver, not a problem maker.

If there is an inefficient system in the hygiene department, develop ways to overcome that inefficiency. Use your head. If you identify a problem and decide that the doctor needs to be involved, come to the discussion table with a solution to offer.

3. Show concern when patients disappoint by assisting business assistants with patient management.

While I do not know of a way to completely eliminate broken appointments, every hygienist needs to understand that downtime is the great destroyer of productivity and profit in a dental practice. One way to help patients understand the importance of continuing care is to give each patient a stated reason for returning. "Mrs. Jones, when you return, I'll be checking that recession (or pockets, cracked tooth, bleeding, etc.) again to see if it has changed." Take responsibility in seeing that patients who disappoint are handled appropriately. Work out a plan that is satisfactory with the doctor.

4. Do not expect other staff members to constantly help you pull your load.

Although you will be an important producer in the practice, please do not succumb to the Ivory Tower complex. Hygienists sometimes start feeling 'self-important' and come to expect other staff members to help them, yet they never offer to help anyone else when the opportunity arises. This is the best way I know of to get your coworkers to resent you. The best offices are those where there is no 'big I, little you,' and each team member works for the good of the practice and not some hidden personal agenda. When others DO help you, show gratitude to them and reciprocate.

5. Go the extra mile with your patients.

Going the extra mile means you go beyond the basics in caring for your patients. An example is when you compose a letter to a specialist when your patient is being referred. You could show a genuine concern for your periodontal patients by checking on those who have to be anesthetized by telephoning them in the evening. If a patient makes mention of an upcoming surgery, make a note and send the patient a get-well card. Always be on the lookout for opportunities to make your patients feel special. Your doctor is sure to appreciate those added touches that show care and concern for his/her patients.

6. Come to work each day looking professional and well groomed.

There is a casual look that is appropriate for outside the office, and there is a professional look that is preferred in a professional environment. When you blur the line between those two looks, it will cost you in respect from your patients. Please avoid the tendency to relax those standards of professionalism that you learned in school regarding your personal appearance. Avoid excessive jewelry, gaudy hairstyles or wet hair, dirty or worn-out shoes, chewing gum, and poor grammar or off-color speech.

7. Keep your operatory neat, clean, and well organized.

Clutter makes your operatory look dirty whether it is or not. Get rid of clutter. As far as possible, maintain clear countertops. Sit in your own treatment chair from time to time and critique your operatory for cleanliness. If a patient perceives your operatory to be dusty or dirty, the patient may make the mental jump to thinking your work is substandard.

8. Promote the doctor's restorative/cosmetic services.

Doctors vary greatly in treatment philosophy. Some doctors will want you to identify needs and let them recommend treatment. Other doctors will want something else to be done. Some practices that are niched in the cosmetic dentistry market may want you to learn to be involved with imaging or digital photography. If your employer has not expressed his/her wishes to you regarding recommending treatment to patients, take the initiative to find out what the doctor wants.

9. If the doctor comes to you with a problem about your work that needs a solution, do not become defensive.

Try to walk in the doctor's shoes. If you need to make a correction, just do it. Show the doctor that you are interested in the business side of your department. Consider how you would feel if you owned the business.

10. Use downtime wisely.

I hope downtime will not be a problem in your office. However, if your doctor is paying you an hourly or daily rate, he has to pay you even if you are not producing. Therefore, it is imperative that you use any downtime you have as productively as possible. If you want to cause your doctor extreme consternation and frustration, just head to the staff lounge and relax with a magazine or handheld computer during downtime. Or you could make several personal telephone calls, text or e-mail your friends, or stand around up at the front desk and engage in chit-chat that wastes the business assistant's time, too.

The Consummate Dental Hygienist

In Conclusion

The profession of dental hygiene is a wonderful career that can give you many years of good compensation and professional gratification. It's all about helping people! There's no greater feeling for a hygienist than the satisfaction that comes from taking a patient from a state of disease to a state of good health through a series of appointments. Additionally, you will develop close personal relationships with many of your patients. They trust their care to you, and you take care of them. Those relationships are a big part of the reason you get up and go to work. Remember, it's a journey. Best wishes to you as you continue down the road.

NOTES

Appendix A

SAMPLE ASSISTED HYGIENE SCHEDULE USING TWO OPERATORIES

Room 1	Fee	Personnel	Room 2	Fee	Personnel
8:00 Recall 1 - seat, greet, update		A			
8:10	1110	93			H
8:20	274	70	H	Perio Patient, seat, update		A
8:30	120	45	H	OHI review, disclose, anesthetize		A
8:40 OHI, Dr. exam		A	Perio scaling		H
8:50 Reappoint, dismiss		A		4341	220	H
9:00					H
9:10					H
9:20 Recall 3 - seat, update		A			A
9:30	1110	93	H	Dismiss, reschedule		A
9:40	120	45	H			
9:50		H	Recall 4, seat, update, X-rays		A
10:00		A		1110	93	H
10:10 Reappoint, dismiss		A		274	70	H
10:20				120	45	H
10:30					H
10:40 Perio or recall 5		A	Dismiss, reschedule		A
10:50	4910	129	H			
11:00	180	75	H	Sealant or child prophy, seat		A
11:10		H	1351 X 4	200	H
11:20 Dr. exam, dismiss, reappoint		A			H
11:30 room set-up					H
11:40			Dismiss, reschedule		A
11:50					
12:00 LUNCH					
12:10					
12:20					
12:30					
12:40					
12:50		A			
1:00 Recall 7		A			
1:10	1110	93	H			
1:20	274	70	H	Recall 8		A
1:30	120	45	H		1110	93	H
1:40 Dismiss, reappoint		A		274	70	H
1:50				120	45	H
2:00 Recall 9		A			A
2:10	1110	93	H	Dismiss, reschedule		
2:20	274	70	H			
2:30	120	45	H	Recall 10		A
2:40		H		1110	93	H
2:50 Dismiss, reappoint		A		120	45	H
3:00					H
3:10 Recall 11		A	Dismiss, reschedule		A
3:20	1110	93	H			
3:30	120	45	H	Recall 12		A
3:40		H		1110	93	H
3:50 Dismiss, reappoint		A		272	50	H
4:00				120	45	H
4:10 Recall 13		A	Dismiss, reschedule		A
4:20	1120	72	H			
4:30	1203	35	H			
4:40	272 + 120	80	H			
4:50 Dismiss, reappoint		H/A			
5:00 Total prod. this column	1291		Total prod. this column	1162	
			Total Production	$2,453	

Appendix B

INFORMED CONSENT FOR DENTAL WORK ON MY CHILD

I have been informed that the following procedures are necessary for my child:

_____

_____

Although every effort will be made to adhere to the proposed treatment plan, unforeseen circumstances or conditions may require a departure from the plan.

After treatment, your child may experience pain and swelling. There is a possibility that the child may bite the inside of the mouth or tongue before the anesthesia wears off, and that the child must be instructed not to do so.

In addition to local anesthetic, nitrous oxide (laughing gas) is frequently used to make the dental visit less stressful. Although the child is usually alert and awake upon leaving the office, there rare instances of lingering sedation.

If I do not remain in the dental office while my child is receiving dental treatment, I am leaving the treatment up to the doctor's judgment and experience and understand that other treatment may have to be rendered. In case it is necessary to contact me during my child's dental visit, my cell phone number is_____.

Child's Name_____

Parent or Guardian's Name_____

Date_____

NOTES

NOTES